PENGUIN A

RABDA

A devotee of Sai Baba of Shirdi, Ruzbeh N. Bharucha is one of the most influential spiritual writers of our times. He is the author of eleven books, including the bestselling *The Fakir* trilogy, which has been translated into several languages.

Formerly a journalist, he is also a documentary filmmaker. His documentary *Sehat . . . Wings of Freedom*, on AIDS and HIV in Tihar Prison, was selected and screened for the XVII International AIDS Conference in 2008. His articles have been published in various publications, including the *Times of India*, *Free Press*, *Indian Express*, *Maharashtra Herald*, *Sunday Observer*, *Jam-e-Jamshed* and *Afternoon*.

His book *My God Is a Juvenile Delinquent* has been included in the reading list of all judicial academies.

Ruzbeh is also the 110th Master for 'The Speaking Tree' where he writes an immensely popular blog on spirituality.

He lives in Pune with his family.

RABDA

My Sai . . . My Sigh

RUZBEH N. BHARUCHA

PENGUIN
ANANDA

PENGUIN ANANDA

Published by the Penguin Group

Penguin Books India Pvt. Ltd, 7th Floor, Infinity Tower C, DLF Cyber City,
Gurgaon 122 002, Haryana, India

Penguin Group (USA) Inc., 375 Hudson Street, New York, New York 10014, USA

Penguin Group (Canada), 90 Eglinton Avenue East, Suite 700, Toronto,
Ontario, M4P 2Y3, Canada

Penguin Books Ltd, 80 Strand, London WC2R 0RL, England

Penguin Ireland, 25 St Stephen's Green, Dublin 2, Ireland (a division of
Penguin Books Ltd)

Penguin Group (Australia), 707 Collins Street, Melbourne, Victoria 3008, Australia

Penguin Group (NZ), 67 Apollo Drive, Rosedale, Auckland 0632, New Zealand

Penguin Books (South Africa) (Pty) Ltd, Block D, Rosebank Office Park,
181 Jan Smuts Avenue, Parktown North, Johannesburg 2193, South Africa

Penguin Books Ltd, Registered Offices: 80 Strand, London WC2R 0RL, England

First published in Penguin Ananda by Penguin Books India 2014

Copyright © Ruzbeh N. Bharucha 2014

10 9 8 7 6 5 4 3 2 1

ISBN 9780143423867

Typeset in Sabon by R. Ajith Kumar, New Delhi
Printed at Thomson Press India Ltd, New Delhi

A PENGUIN RANDOM HOUSE COMPANY

To

The Universal Mother Goddess and our Creator

Sai Baba of Shirdi

All Divine, Perfect, Ancient, Ascended Masters

Archangels and Angels

Celestial, Terrestrial, Physical Warriors of Light

The Oneness Family

Each moment, every single moment, we either create a dream or a nightmare, as each moment we either choose to live or we choose to kill the opportunity to live.

Baba Sai entered the hospital room. He looked at the man lying on a bed, assorted tubes in his body slowly injecting all that could keep him alive. The Old Man smiled.

'Rabda, when will you stop dying and begin to live, my boy?'

The Old Man looked at Rabda, whose hair had streaks of white. As always, Rabda had long hair. His face was gaunt but he looked peaceful in his enforced sleep. A guitar was propped up on the sofa, which was a few feet away from the bed. The guitar had a Cross, the symbol of the Goddess, which resembled the Star of David, the Asho Farohar, the Zoroastrian winged symbol of accession, and Sai Baba of Shirdi's face in various hues of white, saffron and green. The guitar was recognized by music lovers all over the world. It represented not only Oneness but also the music the man—who now lay on a bed, a few breaths away from passing on to the other world—stood for. He made God and the Oneness Family sound groovy. He made religion and spirituality look cool.

Baba Sai walked towards the man He called Rabda. Though the world knew Rabda as Dust, his real name was Caiz.

Baba Sai caressed Rabda's head. Then the Old Man whispered something in Rabda's ear and then stood back and smiled.

Now the fun would begin. This man had always made Baba smile and sigh. But then most of His kids made Him smile and sigh. In reality all of His creations made Him smile and sigh and sometimes they made Him want to scream but then that's another story for another time.

The man born as Caiz, who chose the name Dust, sat upright with a gasp, as though somebody had passed a goodish amount of untamed electrical current through his unmentionables.

'What the . . .' He stopped mid-sentence. Caiz looked around. He sniffed. There was something in the air, some fragrance—sort of loban and uddh that fakirs burnt—and the smell of tobacco and hmm . . . the gorgeous sweetish fragrance of hashish.

He could for some reason see more clearly, as though even the night had a brighter shade of darkness.

He felt lighter. Oh yes, far lighter than he had ever felt— as though for the first time he was out of prison, out of the physical cage that was called his body.

He felt good!

'What the . . .' He looked around. He wasn't supposed to feel good or free. He was supposed to feel dead. He had swallowed forty tablets, or was it forty-five? The number of vodka shots he had consumed would truly decide how many tablets he had swallowed. Was it eight shots or nine? Every time he had a shot of vodka he dunked in five tablets.

Two things he was clear about. He would never drink that brand of vodka again and, yes, for sure, he would have to think of a better way to swallow sleeping pills. Swallowing so many pills was a nasty affair.

'But . . . I mean . . . what the . . .' He still couldn't tell where he was. He couldn't be in his house, he would have heard the waves. He wasn't in anybody else's home when he went about polishing off the vodka bottle and the laughable sleeping pills.

He was going to nail Mike's family jewels to the floor for suggesting such an impotent brand of sleeping pills.

So where was he? He looked around repeatedly, like a puppy that has woken up in a different home—very curious but completely confused.

'And how is my Rabda?'

The Old Man materialized in front of the younger man, who was seated on the bed. A second after the younger man saw and heard Baba Sai, he literally jumped out of his body.

Dust looked at the Old Man, shut his eyes and opened them. He sighed with relief. Baba Sai wasn't there. All this was a dream. Then he heard a chuckle from behind him. Dust slowly, very slowly, turned around and exhaled. Baba Sai stood once again in front of him with a broad grin on His face.

'We can play this game for eternity, bachcha. You pretending that I am not there—around you and in front of you and beside you—and me making it more and more difficult for you to not acknowledge my presence.'

Caiz shut his eyes.

This is all a dream. It has to be a dream. I will wake up in my own bed; obviously the freaking booze and tablets haven't worked, so I am just hallucinating. Why am I seeing Baba standing in front of me with a big, fat, smug grin on His darling face!

'I fathom not, but Caiz, you dehydrated yak, wake up fast.'

Oh yes, Baba Sai was the last thing on my mind before I had the feast of sleeping pills with a dash of vodka, so mystery solved.

One wouldn't blame the man for thinking he was hallucinating. The last thing on his mind when he went about demolishing the vodka bottle and the many strips of sleeping pills was Baba Sai. When the vodka and sleeping pills began to assert their presence and influence him and his anatomy, the man's own music composition—a worldwide hit called 'Singing the Blues with Sai the Baba'—was, with the strange irony of nature, also called life, being aired on a music channel. So the irony was that while Caiz drifted closer to his death, his composition about Sai Baba of Shirdi was playing in the background—on television—and thus Baba Sai was on his mind, heart, lips.

Yes, yes, yes, no wonder I am dreaming of the Old Man. He was on my mind, the last words on my lips and the last sigh in my heart, before I went to sleep. There's another song to this, Caiz, but now go back to sleep and wake up and promise yourself you will not try to kill yourself for another year, or at least until you have researched what is the fastest and surest way to freaking kill yourself successfully.

So Caiz shut his eyes, took a deep breath and realized he had begun to float towards the ceiling.

'Yikes!' he screamed out loud. 'Go down boy, down, there's a very unclean fan revolving at a few knots an hour, enough to give you the cleanest shave in history. Down boy, down . . .'

'Rabda, will you please come down and have a man-to-man talk with me?'

Caiz looked at Baba who was still respecting the laws of gravity while he continued to move, heaven- or fan-bound. He looked around frantically, and that is when he saw something he would never forget. He saw himself lying on the bed, with tubes inserted into his body, including his mouth, and a ventilator pumping air into him. That brought him back to earth fast and good. He walked towards his body and looked at himself. Apart from appearing peaceful, he looked like crap, he had to admit. He looked old. He looked haggard. He looked like an ageing hippy.

Caiz looked back and saw Baba Sai standing and smiling.

'Even if this is a nightmare, a Master shouldn't be smiling at such a time, when a man sees himself lying horizontal, with tubes and wires shoved into his body through every conceivable opening. I mean this is a dream . . . I mean a nightmare, right Baba? . . . but it can't be a nightmare if You are present, but You know what I mean.'

'My child, each moment, every single moment, we either create a dream or a nightmare, as each moment we either choose to live or we choose to kill the opportunity to live. Each moment you are living, if you are giving life your very best, no matter the knocks you receive as a consequence of fate or your own free will, you are creating another future karmic nightmare—or dying, as stagnation is death. No nightmare is worse than that of being stagnant, and carping and cribbing and slandering; when you go through life in a stagnant haze, a haze of boredom, sloth, anger, greed, lust, listlessness, slander, jealousy, you, each moment, become the architect of dreams and hope and life or the captain of a shipwrecked, battered heap of degradation—the perfect harbinger of joy and peace or a doom-smith of future karmic nightmares.'

Caiz looked at Baba and sighed.

'Ehhhh. I haven't understood a darn word You've said to me, my Sai. That could be because I am truly high and asleep or I may be dead, and I am sure the small print on the karmic memorandum of understanding, which either I didn't read or have forgotten while signing up for this song and dance called life, is going to hurt like the dickens.'

The door suddenly opened and Caiz turned around. He saw his bandmates enter. The bastards were drunk too, he sighed.

They too serve the Lord who toil honestly and selflessly, spreading the sigh of the Lord to all they meet and help.

Caiz saw the boys enter. All grown men, in their late forties and early fifties, the drummer in his early sixties, and he couldn't help but smile. Whether he was alive or dead, dreaming or hallucinating, the boys always made him smile and laugh. They had not known each other for long—a decade—but during that time had spent enough time together to constitute a lifetime. They composed music, gossiped, travelled, and just hung around with each other.

Caiz was a known name—he had been nominated for international awards, won three, and not attended any of the award functions—and his group had not won any awards but millions of hearts all over the world. Theirs was . . . call it 'fusion-Sufi-bhakti' music with a lot of blues, soft rock and abuses off and on thrown in.

They were the bad boys of spiritual music, quite a facade as they were in reality damaged goods, barely able to wake up in the morning without some part of the anatomy mysteriously insisting on throwing in the towel. Often when they were seated in cafes, speaking with great passion

7

or having an animated discussion, the usual refrain which circulated was that they were caught in the embrace of inspiration, when in reality they, more often than not, were really just exchanging notes on arthritis, bowel movements, ulcers and the futility of existence.

The futility of existence had always plagued Caiz. When he was seven years old, he sat in front of a hill, looked at the sunset as the sky was splashed with hues of orange and red, and shut his eyes and wondered what the hell he was doing in his body.

He was sure that he wasn't supposed to be in the body and that the body was a cage imprisoning him. For some reason, even at the age of seven, Caiz was reminded of a very philosophical line said by one sage to another. So these two sages are seated, naked as skinned chickens in a butcher's shop, high up in the Himalayas, in a cave from where they cannot descend now, making it easier for them to achieve liberation uninterrupted and after a few days come to the spiritual conclusion that their breathing technique which was supposed to raise their body temperature actually reduced the heat after a few hours of breathe in . . . breathe out . . . It was then that this sage said the famous words: 'Brother, I believe it is safe to say that for the next few decades we are screwed.'

Caiz empathized with the sages. Since the age of seven he had felt trapped in the body, a deep void within him, knowing for sure that this wasn't home and this wasn't his natural state of being.

So his music flowed and was played in temples and even dargahs and people were inspired to become better human beings and happiness and Oneness were experienced and Caiz went deeper into the abyss of Nothingness. The plot weakened and the embrace of cold darkness grew more passionate.

His friends, each one, gathered around him, aware that this night had to come, that it had been waiting to come for a while now, but one of them seeing their friend on the bed with tubes and all broke down and the other men didn't know what to do. They continued to look at their friend and then they sat, some on the sofa, some on the ground and they opened another bottle of Caiz's favourite drink and passed the bottle around, each saying Caiz's favourite words whenever he said a goodbye to them: 'See you when I see you, brothers.'

Baba and Caiz noticed the men and Caiz smiled and turned towards Baba.

'This ranks as the corniest dream I have ever had, Baba.'

'Come, let me make it more corny.'

The next thing Caiz knew was that he was standing in a cave, with a fire burning, and there was nothing to be seen around but mountains and that they were away from civilization and, in fact, away from it all. He looked at Baba first, then the Fire, then he walked towards the edge of the cave, and it took his breath away. There was snow all around, and as far as the eye could see it was just mountains, high mountains, as the valley below wasn't even visible. They were so high up there that Caiz realized that just maybe nobody had ever, ever set foot here. Nobody could have, as it was impossible to be able to climb these mountains. Unless of course you are the Sai of Shirdi along with a completely drunk man, high on bad vodka and lousy sleeping pills.

What Caiz noticed was that the moment they came into the cave, Baba became radiant and it was as though sparks flew from Him and also from the ether sparks flew back into Him.

It was as though He was a softly glowing fire, a golden fire, with rays or sparks of light entering and leaving Him continuously. The more Caiz observed Baba the more He realized how much he loved the Old Man. Baba was dressed in a long white robe, His head covered with a white cloth, the robe torn in a few places, but the Divine Radiance that emitted from and covered Baba made you think He was all golden fire.

Baba prepared a chillum, smoked for a while, and then handed it to Caiz, who was not new to smoking chillums either, and for a while the Master and the very confused man smoked, passing the chillum back and forth.

Peace is a state of mind. Bliss is a state of being.

'What are these sparks coming out of you and the innumerable ones moving back into you, Baba?'

Baba smiled and when He smiled you felt the whole world melt away. Rabda had never seen a smile so beautiful in all his life and was certain he would never see a smile so sublime.

'Let me make you understand it in the language you will. You have a satellite in space, which transmits whatever it has to to the main receiver, which is located someplace on Mother Earth, which then transmits images or sound or whatever to individual recipients. Be it your television, your mobile phones, your computer, whatever. All these things were first created for spirituality and then brought down thousands of years later to facilitate communication and in reality, Oneness, though of course things have not really worked as per the plans of the Elders.'

Baba used a lot of Sufi words, many Arabic words and often Sanskrit too. He spoke in English, Hindi, Marathi, Gujarati and Urdu, and inexplicably Rabda understood all perfectly. He did not understand how he could comprehend all these languages, but obviously Baba wanted him to

11

understand every word He spoke and so Rabda understood it all.

'We have the Almighty, whom I call the Fakir, who is also called Deva, Devi, Khuda, Ahura, Rama, Krishna, God, Allah. The focus of each and every living being is to merge into the Fakir. The role of every Guru or Master is to make each disciple into a Master and to eventually help the disciple merge with the One. But there are many Perfect Masters, who because of the love of Their children will not merge with the Absolute One for the simple reason that once you merge with the Almighty, you become the Almighty yourself. The drop becomes the ocean and the ocean merges into the drop too and there is only Oneness. But the Almighty has set rules and S(H)e too becomes bound by the rules.

'The principal of a school sets the rules and regulations for the school, for how each student progresses to a higher class or stays in the same class, and the rules cannot be changed for anybody as justice is paramount. But the principal is not involved in the day-to-day functioning of the classroom. Only the teachers are involved. Whom to pass and whom to fail is the teacher's prerogative. If a student fails, the parents cannot approach the principal to appeal for the child, to allow the child to move ahead. Irrespective of the child's ability, circumstance or aptitude, if he has failed he stays in the same class. But let us say a teacher sees aptitude in a student, sees the student working hard, and, for some reason—say, medical, or the child is a slow starter—irrespective of how the child has performed, manipulates the mark sheet and lets the child move to a higher class. The teacher is involved in the day-to-day activities of the child and knows the child like nobody else does, perhaps even better than the parents and family. The child's future really is in the hands of the teacher, the Guru.

'The love for teaching and seeing a child progress prompts many teachers not to get into administration and to even turn down the post of principal, as a principal's hands are tied. A principal cannot be partial. Similarly, though many spiritual Perfect Masters can merge with the Almighty, They choose, because of Their love for Their children, to remain Masters and not merge with the Almighty. I have promised my children that I will come running to help whoever calls out to me, and if karma necessitates that the child go through the ordeal or experience, I shall stand by the child and be with him and go through the ordeal or experience with him, giving him strength, wisdom and grace to go through his lot with calmness and pure surrender. Of course, that is if the child allows me to help him go through the experience calmly.

'So if the Almighty is on the twelfth dimension, Perfect Masters reside on the eleventh dimension, one rung below. My real essence is on the eleventh dimension. That in your parlance would be the Mother Satellite. Then you have the receiver. Masters have two receivers. One is what you see in front of you. This is my cave. I have materialized in the body and remain away from all, operating from here. This body did not come to receive you. My spark came to receive you. My spark is my energy that is me, without the physicality involved. I sit here and countless sparks go out of me and countless sparks merge back into me. The world has its own vibrations and the Master would get depleted if He or She were to venture forth in that vibration. So our energy goes forth, but just a spark or, as one says, just an anksh, a part of me. That part of me is the whole of me but still only a part of me. A drop is part of the ocean and the ocean is in the drop too. So the first receiver is this body of mine you see now and through the receiver countless people receive my Energy.

The second receiver is my samadhi or dargah, which also sends forth waves upon waves of my Energy to all those who come to be cleansed and energized and blessed. The resting place of a Master works as a cleanser, an energizer, a restorer, blessing all those who come from far to seek solace and respite and strength and blessings.

'Then we have helpers, an army of spiritual helpers, each religion will give various names to Them, but let us just stick to Their essence and call Them the army of Light Workers. Most of Them are invisible, They work as guides, guardian angels, healers, counsellors, who work with the individual according to the individual's faith, receptiveness and love. Most often, these beautiful Light Workers were followers of the Master when they were in the body, and have now have taken on the mantle of serving the Master in the spirit dimensions. Of course, there are archangels and djinns and fairies and Elemental Guides or High-Spirit Energies, who have never taken birth in the physical body but continue to serve all of creation, due to Their love for the One.

'The Light Workers are those who are in the physical body, who are themselves working out their karmas but now are operating more from the understanding of Them being spirits in the body, than being just the body. Anybody who works with true selfless love and compassion, lending a helping hand, wiping a tear, working for the downtrodden selflessly, noble nurses, doctors, lawyers, the police force, employers, a sweeper, a cobbler, a homemaker, a rickshaw driver, a man selflessly working to keep the home fires burning, anybody who is genuinely kind at heart, who spreads happiness, peace, joy, harmony, love, without resorting to slander, gossip, hate, greed, envy, jealousy, corruption, all become Light Workers, knowingly or unknowingly. They too serve the Lord who toil honestly and selflessly, spreading the sigh of the Lord to all they meet and help. Yes, being human, they too slip and fall, but their essence is to spread the warmth of the Lord, thus even though they might fall, they quickly get up, and continue to silently work for the Lord.

'So you have me, in my original form, say on the eleventh dimension, seated amongst the Masters, through my essence, my physical self is seated here, from here, countless sparks or energy manifestations are sent to all those who truly need my personal presence, the same works through my tomb, and then to all those who represent the One, through me. When I am called, depending on the relationship and faith and love of the individual, the Energy flows to the individual, which means I or the Perfect Master can be all over creation with His or Her children, whenever one truly calls. The more intense the longing for me, the stronger the manifestation. If you want me to be with you all the time, you need to be with me all the time. The more you want me, the stronger my manifestation grows. If you want me only for a particular reason, I will be with you for that particular reason. But, remember, want me for the right reasons and I will, as Allah is my witness, be with you for ever, very often even materializing in my original form or taking the physical form of a man, woman, child, animal.

'You, like in your last physical birth, once again called out to me, when you were virtually breathing your last. Your call did not come from a selfish reason, but truly came out of love, so I had to come to you. But I always surround my people with my Light Workers, whether you call me or not, who report back to Me and thus I am always aware of each and every thought, word, emotion, intention, of each child of mine. The responsibility of a Guru, a Perfect Master, never ends, till the Perfect Master merges with the Source. Can you imagine the immense love each Perfect Master has for His children, that They put on hold, so often, perpetually, the final merger with Their Most Beloved. I truly hope you have understood at least something I have been going on and on about, for a while.'

Rabda twitched his nose, as if to say, 'Sort of', and Baba chuckled, the most beautiful sound in all creation.

> Do not become a friend of your child as if you too will
> become friends then who will play the role of a parent?
> But treat children with compassion and love as they are
> what parents make them to be.

S ai and Rabda sat in the cave with the Fire burning
between them, providing warmth, light and a beautiful
fragrance. It was a small cave, not more than a few
hundred feet wide and long. Baba always sat facing the south
and the Fire burnt away. He needed nothing for the Fire to
keep raging, just a glance and the Fire did as He wanted.

The sparks moved in and out of Baba and after a while
one got used to this and Baba seemed to be moving about
with wings or in a swirling orbit of Fire. Rabda felt his heart
would burst, due to the intense love and longing that he felt
for the Old Man. He was himself surprised and shocked that
he could love anybody with such passion and selflessness. If
Baba were to tell him to do or not do something, whatever
it may be, there was not a doubt in Rabda's mind that he
would do so or not do so in a blink of an eye. This love he
felt was so new but felt so familiar that Rabda felt restless
and yet at the same time he had never felt such bliss—yes,
not peace, but bliss.

Peace is a state of mind. Bliss is a state of being.

'Nobody is concerned about who I am or the essence of my being along my journey but all seem to be so interested in whether I am a Muslim or a Hindu. I am just a servant and slave of Allah.'

'Nope. You are not considered to be a servant or slave of Allah, Baba Sai, on earth; in India, you have been made into an avatar. Some consider you to be a Lord Shiva Avatar, some a Lord Rama Avatar, some a Lord Datta Avatar and some a Lord Krishna Avatar.'

'What about Lord Brahma Avatar? They forgot poor Lord Brahma?' Baba chuckled.

'Poor Lord Brahma is not on the top of the charts where spirituality is concerned.'

'Whose avatar do you consider me, Rabda?'

'I consider you to be my Baba. I don't care a flying duck whether you are an avatar or a maha avatar or this or that or whatever. You are my Baba Sai. My rockstar. My lead guitarist. My main lyricist. My only manager and choreographer and everything. You are the words in my song and the rhythm in my melody. You are the thump in my bass guitar and the beat in the drums. You are my father, mother, friend, the sigh in my soul and the thud in my heart and very often an excruciating pain in my very being and a migraine in my head. Life without you is like the most delicious mango but without any taste in my tongue or the whiff of anything, least of all Your fragrance. You are for me the Fakir, not this fancy Hindu God all decked up in finery and seated under a gold roof, nor a Muslim who follows the code of conduct and behaviour prescribed by the Holy Quran. For me you are my be-all and end-all, the Universe and beyond the beyond,

You who have allowed everybody and anybody to thrust their beliefs and their fundas on to You.'

Baba Sai filled another chillum and took a deep puff and handed the pipe to Rabda. Both men smoked quietly. For some reason it was neither cold nor hot. It was neither day nor night. It was surreal and Rabda never ever wanted to wake up.

'Bachcha, sometimes I feel the purpose of my coming in the form of Sai Baba of Shirdi has got negated as my teachings and my very essence has been forgotten. I spent my entire life in Shirdi, as a fakir, wearing a white robe, which was torn or stitched in so many places that it looked like thatched cloth. The essence of a fakir or a yogi is to embrace poverty, as the material world has a way of caging you with its charms and its illusions. The very word *fakir* comes from the word *faqr*, which means poverty. A fakir is said to embrace poverty willingly and lovingly; to embrace poverty means to drop all worldly attachments, as it is worldly attachments that stand between an individual and Allah. This poverty that we talk about is enforced—we eat little, talk little, sleep little. We are meant to not take up poverty for any other reason but that it is a way to go beyond any kind of attachment. If a fakir takes up poverty but keeps yearning for good food and clothes, a comfortable accommodation and life, then the very reason for which the fakir has taken the path of embracing poverty becomes meaningless. I lived my life according to the tenets or tariqat laid down by the Sufi tradition, from the time of Prophet Mohammed and the yogis, starting with Lord Datta. Every religion prescribes that the spiritual aspirant or seeker become detached. Lord Buddha too took up poverty and the begging bowl. So did Lord Mahavir. This is our tradition. To embrace poverty willingly and to keep the focus on the fakir is one of the main foundations of spiritual seekers. Embracing poverty is better than being a king and it is countless times superior to being rich. But the main reason is go beyond the material and focus on the One.

'Now when a person is living the life of a householder, he or she cannot afford to abide by this philosophy of voluntary poverty.'

'Oh, for sure. If the poor chap wants to practise being a fakir, apart from voluntary poverty, he will experience involuntary flogging every moment of his existence from his more dangerous half!'

'Humour truly isn't your strong point, na Rabda?'

Both the men looked at each other and began to laugh.

'Yes, it is not right for an individual to embrace voluntary poverty if living the life of a householder, but, son, you still are not getting the essence of being a fakir. A fakir practises voluntary poverty not because he loves to live in poverty, but because he wants to be detached from all worldly attachments as it is worldly attachments which eventually enslave one and all, and cut the wings with which one would soar towards Him. So, one can be in the world but devoid of any attachments. If that is the case then one may be surrounded by luxury but detached and thus still be a fakir in essence, and one can be a fakir and still crave for comfort and be a householder in essence.

'So the sad part is that the world has made Fakir Sai into a God surrounded by comfort and luxury. The pomp and gold is not for One who has gone beyond all this.'

'But now You no longer can be called a fakir. You are God. And the way You are worshipped, You have taken place in the top brackets, reserved for Gods worshipped by Hindus.'

'If I wanted to divulge my religion, I would have. The reason I did not divulge my birth or religion is that a fakir or a yogi has no religion, Faqiri itself is our religion and we are born when we meet our Guru or when we realize Oneness with the Fakir. Thus I have never disclosed by birth or religion. How hard can it be for everybody to realize that there must have been a reason for me not to reveal who I was?

'Initially in Shirdi there would be countless fakirs coming over. Sufis abounded in Shirdi. They came to me for guidance and for spiritual strength and knowledge. Often on the path of spirituality, one gets stuck. Fakirs would come from far and wide and be guided by me. Yes, with them I spoke in Urdu or Arabic. I would wear anklets and dance and do the Sufi swirling. I have spoken a lot about the Holy Quran to them and the principles of Sufism and how to move beyond everything and focus on the One. If any one of them had kept a record of all that I said to these fakirs and Sufis, then for sure I would be considered a Sufi and thus a Muslim. Have you read the hundred and more pages that Abdul, who took care of my physical needs and wants, kept of all that I told Him? If you read what I have dictated to Abdul, you will say Baba Sai is a Muslim. But as there is not much recorded of what transpired between the Sufis and fakirs and Me but there is a lot of record of all that I told my Hindu devotees and disciples, it seems I am a Hindu. But the fact is till the last ten years of my being in the physical body, apart from families living in and near Shirdi, I would only get fakirs and

Sufis coming from far and wide to meet me. It was in the last ten years, say since 1908, that my children from Bombay and other parts of the country began to come to me. Most of them belonged to the Hindu faith and there were many who kept diaries, and most of those who wrote books about me too were from the Hindu faith. The Sufis and fakirs travelled far and wide and thus they were not really spoken to when these books were being written. Therefore, if the books are read it will seem that I was well versed with the ancient and venerated books of Hinduism and thus I was assumed to be a Hindu.

'But why would I tell a Hindu to read the Holy Quran? Have I lost my mind? Why would I quote from the Quran passages to my Hindu disciples? And why would I tell my Muslim disciples to read sacred books passed down through the generations, written or spoken by sages? One respects the faith of all, and one quotes from the books of those one is familiar with. If a Hindu came to me, I would tell the child to read works from the ancient sages. If a Muslim came to me, I would quote from the Quran and tell the person to recite a paragraph from the Quran.'

'But so many saw You as their God. You were seen as Lord Datta, Shri Rama, Lord Shiva, Lord Vithal . . .'

'Of course I will be seen in any and every form, as once you swim in the Great Ocean you can resemble anything that has come out from the Great Ocean. My children saw me in the image of their God and thus I became the image of their God.'

And saying this Baba began to change His form. Every known God, Prophet, Goddess, Guru, Perfect Master, He became and metamorphosed into.

'This is not new. Every Perfect Master could take the form of the One the disciple worshipped, trying to tell the disciple and devotee that he or she is me and I am with the One and eventually it is all about Oneness. What I feel sad about is that my essence has been forgotten. I stood for Oneness. In Shirdi, how many Sufis do you see now? I am from the One and the One has no religion. Shirdi has become a pilgrimage dham when in reality Shirdi and Sai Baba should have been a pilgrimage of Oneness. I do not see Oneness now. I see duality.'

'But you allowed formal worship to take place when You were present too?'

'Yes, I am a slave of my children. I will allow everything to take place that makes my children happy. Earlier there used to be recitation of the Quran and Sufi songs sung at sunset time as earlier I was surrounded by Sufis and fakirs. I would dance with them as that is the way of Sufis. A Zoroastrian saw Prophet Zarathustra in me and thus so many Zoroastrians came to me. Christians see Lord Jesus. Whenever anyone came with faith I became one with the One. Shirdi should have become the only place in the world to be a pilgrimage site for all religions. If a statue had to be placed and ritualistic worship had to be done, it could have been done in another place in Shirdi. My tomb should have been left as a simple resting place and a place of healing and Oneness for the countless who come to me, as Their Master and God. My place should have been left as a haven for Oneness. Each one could have come and done their respective prayers and been blessed with whatever they came for. Even now, there should be a time and place for all religious prayers to take place in front of my tomb and statue—Islamic prayers, Zoroastrian prayers, Christian prayers, Sikh prayers and Hindu prayers. I am Oneness. I am the fakir of the Almighty One. As long as my children don't go beyond religion and stop trying to make me an avatar or a pir or a qutub but just love me as Sai, their Father and Mother, my true essence will never be understood. I am His Servant and as His Servant I am the be-all and end-all for my children. I am Sai. What is Sai? Sai means Father? Sai means the Wise One. Sai means the Holy One. Is that not enough for my children? Do I have to be this avatar and that avatar? Can I not just be Sai, the Fakir, and Sai, the One who loves.

'Rabda, understand one thing. Jesus Christ was not a Christian. He was born before Christianity and obviously those who follow Him are called Christians. Jesus was a Jew. And He allowed His own people to crucify Him. Obviously nobody could crucify Him without His permission. So He planned everything down to the last nail. Imagine planning out something for yourself that is going to be so merciless and ruthless but then He had to do what He was told to do by the One. He thus was following the Plan. So did Jews crucify Jesus? No. Jesus planned for Himself to get crucified in order to take on the universal karma of all of creation. So if He planned the merciless torture on Himself for freeing all creation from their karmic baggage and sins and ramifications, He needed somebody to do this to Him. Judas loved Jesus the most amongst Jesus's inner circle. Judas never once thought Jesus would be crucified and when he realized that they were torturing his Jesus, he returned all the gold coins, threw the coins and when nothing was going to stop his Jesus from being crucified, Judas killed himself. So understand those who crucified Jesus, and Judas too played their part. The question to ask is this: if I am going to be crucified, who would I choose to do the needful? Certainly not those I do not know. It will have to be those close to me. For reasons best known to me, I would choose my people to kill me and torture me. I know you might not understand this, but the fact is that all karmic cleansing is done by those who have been closest to us. Not strangers. But those closest to us. So, to somebody blaming the Jews for crucifying Christ, well, the fact is that Christ was a Jew too, so Christ was crucified by His lot.

'Prophet Zarathustra was not a Zoroastrian but those who followed Zarathustra are known as Zoroastrians. The same for Lord Buddha. The same for the Prophet Mohammed. He was not born a Muslim but He introduced Islam and then His followers became Muslims. So for us, religion is ancillary. A Prophet, a Perfect Master, a Saint is beyond religion. What do we have to do with religion? Our bond is with the One, and God has no religion. There is no special heaven for Hindus, or a special one for Muslims, Christians, Zoroastrians, Buddhists, Native Americans. You get what I am saying, boy? All those who try to give me a religion are losing the plot. If I wanted to reveal my religion and birth and parents, I would have. The fact is I am beyond religion. I am merged with the One. The One has no religion. Just as neither the Prophet nor the Master has a religion. We belong to all of creation. All of mankind. We do not belong to one sect of people.

'Do you think Lord Shiva is a Hindu? Obviously not. He

always was. Long before even creation. You think the word Aum is the sole prerogative of Hindus? No. The word Aum is the sound of the cosmos. It is the sigh of creation. It is heard by all those who are connected with the One. What we know as Aum, the Zoroastrians called Ahun and some African sage will call it Ooon, but it is the sound of creation and eventually it is beyond religion.

'As long as my followers, children, lovers, devotees do not understand that I do not need to be a Hindu or a Muslim, I am Sai, the Servant, Slave, Son and Part of the Whole of the One, I am Sai, the One, Sai the Sigh of the One, as long as they do not understand and grasp this simple reality, that I do not need to be an avatar or know all about Islam and the Sufi hierarchy to be Sai, I just need to be loved and loved and loved and loved to be Sai, as long as people do not understand this, my journey and my presence and my essence have all gone to waste. If my people do not go beyond religion, I have failed. Your Sai is a failure if he cannot make his children go beyond religion and for as long as they do not understand that God is beyond religion. And if Sai is their God, how can Sai have a religion, my child? Sai itself is a religion. Sai is the religion of love, brotherhood, compassion and Oneness. I do not need or want to be in any temple. I want to be in the heart of my children. I do not want to be God incarnate. I just want to be loved as Sai Baba, your Father, who is one with God. Who am I? I have come a countless times. More than eighty-four times. Are you saying I came all the time as a Hindu or a Muslim? Why can Sai not be a Zoroastrian, a Christian, a Buddhist? Are you saying I have not been present since the beginning of time? Was their religion from the beginning of time? To cage me in one box means not to know me ever. To still wonder which religion I belong to means not knowing or loving me ever.

'There are so many who have even written about my so-called birth and childhood and parentage and religion. Was I off my head to not have revealed everything to one and all about my religion and birth and everything? Why did I say nothing? Because I believed that my children would only want me. They would not be interested in anything I did not want them to know or be concerned about. But I have failed, Rabda. Failed miserably. The Muslims tell strange stories about me. The Hindus have made me one of them. But is that who I am, Rabda? I belong to all or I belong to nobody but the One. Sai has been forgotten, the politics of Sai has begun. I am a fakir. I have embraced poverty and detachment as I only want Him. What have I to do with things that divide? I have come to unify. I join things. I cannot break things. Nowadays religion has become something to divide brother from brother. Thus, all the more, Sai cannot belong to any religion.

'When my Taj, Tajuddin, left His body, the statue of Lord Vithal and Rukmani Ma wept for twelve hours. It is a fact recorded by even the newspapers of those days. Why would Lord Vishnu and Ma Laxmi weep for Tajuddin if there was no Oneness? My Taj was in the body, a five-times namazi, one who used to initially say namaz or Islamic prayers five times a day and yet Lord Vithal and Rukmani Ma wept for His passing. Why? The answer is simple. There is only Oneness where God, Goddess and Master are concerned. Only mankind divides. God unites. Thus, bachcha, know one thing, if you love Sai, love Oneness. If you love duality throw Sai out of your heart, home and temple. But if you love Oneness, instal Sai as the Embodiment of the One. Then you have every right to pray to me as Sai, Rama, Krishna, Shiva, Dattatreya, Vithal, Mohammed, Ma Laxmi, Christ, Zarathustra, as then praying to me would be praying to all of Them. But if you cannot see my Oneness, then those people are stabbing me repeatedly in my heart. All those who abuse, slander, injure, rape, bomb, maim, kill in God's name belong to the army of shaitan, or the devil himself. More people have been killed in the name of our Lord then killed in the name of the devil. What kind of spirituality or religious sentiment is this? How can you so brazenly kill or hurt in the name of the One who is Love Personified? Every time a Muslim kills in the name of Prophet Mohammed or Allah, he stabs Prophet Mohammed and Allah. Every time a Christian kills in the name of Christ, he puts another nail into Christ. Each time a Hindu kills in the name of Rama, Shiva, Hinduism, he burns all the sacred scriptures of the dharam, and stabs his God in whose name he kills or slanders or harms another soul. All religions on one side are not worth the life of an innocent person for in that innocent person resides God and nothing can weigh heavier than the living God in all beings. Masters and Prophets belong to no religion as we belong to the One. So, bachcha, I am Sai, the One beyond religion.'

They sat down. Baba was in dhyan and more and more flames shot out of His body and many more returned into His body. Rabda sat and saw Baba and he felt days and nights passed with him just looking at his Master, God, Goddess, but, most important, his Baba Sai.

> Either you believe that God does not exist, there is no
> Supreme Power running this grand show, or you believe
> in a just God. You cannot believe in a God who exists
> but is unjust.

'Okay, two questions, Baba Sai, before I wake up?
You told me I had tried to commit suicide even
in my last lifetime and You spoke about a book
kept by Abdul. You want to talk about those things?'

'Okay, first and foremost, let it be understood that suicide
is the worst possible punishment you can give yourself. The
state of the being who has committed suicide is so lost that
it can wander aimlessly for aeons as an earthbound spirit,
always rooted to the spot where he ended his life forcefully.
You must understand one thing: free will sometimes
transcends even one's karmic blueprint. Each individual has
certain phases where the individual can pass over or can
then continue living. Each individual has three such yogs
or phases. Even if an individual attempts suicide and it is
attempted not in these yogs or phases, he will not succeed
in his attempt and could land up in a very dire state. Out of
ten suicide attempts, nearly eight fail, and out of those eight
failures, at least half scar you for life and leave a very bad
physical impact, in which anything from paralysis to burnt

intestines can result, but worse, now you have to live your life as an invalid. Secondly, if suicide is attempted in the yogs or phases, there are chances the individual will pass over, but the spirit will linger on till the person's natural time to leave the body is destined. So if an individual commits suicide at the age of twenty but his lifespan is that of eighty, for the next sixty years the spirit of the individual will be earthbound, in all probability rooted to the same spot, reliving those last moments for the next sixty years.

'The worst part is that the individual is so saddened or depressed or angry or filled with a state of hopelessness or anger or frustration or playing the victim that he will not be able to set himself free from those last tragic moments and thus will go through hell for the next few decades—and if that is not hell, what is? Remember, hell is a state of mind. You and only you are responsible for giving yourself a heavenly state of being or one filled with hell-like domination. One must really hate oneself to commit suicide. Do you understand me? Also, because the individual is so closed off, nine out of ten times he refuses help from family and friends, who are now in the spirit world. The individual thinks he or she is sleeping and will wake up or the aura is so closed that nobody can help the individual. There are negative spirits that abound amongst creation, waiting to latch on to and use another spirit for their nefarious intentions. Once the individual gets into the clutches of these spirits, there is hell to pay, which I cannot begin to describe.

'Thus, suicide is not a good way to love yourself or escape from whatever problems you are besieged with, as the earthbound state is a thousand times worse and what is worse is that you will have to eventually come back into the physical body and go through, in a more intense manner, the same experience from which you had tried to run away when you committed suicide. Do you understand, you demented frog?

'That makes me feel so much better, Baba, such comforting words.'

'Now why are you with me? The answer is simple. I have promised you that no matter what, you will always be with me. It is a promise I gave you and you seem to be making the most of it. I do not give this promise too often as free will can turn an individual into something completely different from who he is and can mar all spiritual potential and liberation. But you have bound me up with your love and devotion from your past lives and I have promised you that no matter what, when you pass over and when you are in the body, I will be with you. And thus you seem to have made suicide you destructive hobby.

'So you are one of the few fortunate ones who come to me. Yes, prayers, intentions, past-life associations can help the soul who has committed suicide, but how does a person know whether prayers, intentions, past-life associations are going to help in a guaranteed manner? You get my point, you worm? Anybody who commits suicide is asking for hell. Yes, the Master is all-merciful but usually the individual is so caught up with grief and fear that the individual refuses to accept any help from the Master or his or her loved ones who are now in the spirit world. It is a sad situation.'

'How did I manage to extract a promise from you?'

'More than seven centuries ago, I was a seeker, who had

done tremendous tapasya or penance and prayers. I was in a cave. I was told by my Master that it was time for me to go back to the world and serve all beings. I was like a skeleton. I came down the mountain and people thought I was a madman. They began to throw stones at me and even let their dogs on me. You were a boy of ten who for some reason took pity on me and fought the dogs, threw stones back at the people and somehow managed to get me to a safe place. You nursed me and you saved my life. You took care of me for fourteen days and nourished my body and won my soul. When the time came to part, I told you that whenever you were to think of me, my God, Goddess and Master, along with me, would be there in spirit to assist you and be with you. You said that you wanted me to be with you always in spirit and whenever you were to die, I would come to take you and keep you with me. I must have been out of mind or the fasting and penance must have affected my damn brain and common sense! I agreed to always be with you and come for you and keep you with me, and so here we are. When you saw me for the first time you called me Rabda, meaning "God's Being" or "One who belongs to God", and since the centuries, because of my promise to you and your being blessed with God, Goddess, my Master and my presence and embrace, I decided this name suited you better. You belong to me and I am with you always, and since then I have called you Rabda. If I knew what a nuisance you were, I would have pleaded for those people to begin to throw stones at you instead!'

'Basically You are stuck with me. Hmmmm . . . That's really dandy!'

'So anyway, you seem to have fallen in love with me since the first time you saved me and after a few days you ran away from home, found me and stayed with me. You served me and would not leave my sight. And since then I have been trying to get rid of you but you like a spiritual leech are bloody persistent.

'Last lifetime, you committed suicide and you were better at the job. You succeeded. But you did not commit suicide for any other reason but because you did not want to live away from me. And your parents were against me as according to them I was a Muslim and a madman. Your parents worked for a British officer who was very fond of you. He taught you English and he was very keen that you study and then leave for England with him and his children. His wife had died a year ago due to cholera. Your parents wanted you to go to England and start a life there. You were around eighteen at that time and you were called Lal with love by one and all.'

'Maybe I committed suicide because of such an oddball name, Baba.'

'Oh, why do I get the crazies, I still have not understood. So now keep quiet. Lal means beloved. Not lal as in red colour, you idiot!'

'Ohhhhh, lal even means the colour red. This is becoming a nightmare. Hello, Mr Reddish Beloved.'

'Rabda, you are aware I can turn you into any of the many species available on the menu card of evolution, right?'

'Yes, Mr Gold Father, as you are golden in colour and my dad.'

'Allah! The price one pays to become a Master. So anyway, you realized that there was no way you could live your life without me. You had grown up seeing me in Shirdi. You used to spend time cleaning the Masjid Ayi [Baba always called the masjid Masjid Ayi, but now it is known as Dwarka Mai as once a devotee wanted to go to Dwarka to pay homage to Lord Krishna and Baba Sai calmly told him, this Masjid Mai is Dwarka Mai] and doing odd jobs for me. I was considered a madman then. Used to sit under a tree or roam about in the jungle without a thought in the world for my well-being and comfort or safety. I used to sit under a tree and meditate for hours on end. My hair was so long it reached nearly the back of my knees. I was living spiritually in a God-intoxicated state and it would take time for me to assimilate God-realization with human consciousness.

'You knew me since then. You used to spend time looking at me from far. When children and others made fun of me or ridiculed me, you fought on my behalf. You used to help Bayaja Ma find me so that she could feed me and then break her fast, even if it meant that she would go hungry till late afternoon as I had the habit of wandering about or selecting a place of isolation to just be.

'So, anyway, when you were fourteen your parents left Shirdi and you were taken to Thane, Bombay. Your parents were very loving but very strict. The Englishman was very loving but needed you as a son and a caretaker for his motherless children. One girl, aged six, and a younger boy, aged four. They loved you. So they wanted you with them and then to take you with them to England. Your parents were ecstatic and made it clear that if you did not go with the Englishman, they were as good as dead for you. One night, knowing that peanuts were as good as poison for you as you were very allergic to peanuts, you ground some peanuts and ate a bagful. Then, not wanting your parents or the Englishman to feel you had committed suicide, you cleaned up and, shutting your eyes and remembering me, you suffocated to death. You were barely eighteen or nineteen then. The next morning they found you dead. Those days if they found a person dead, there was no medical investigation.

'The Englishman left India in a short time and your parents lived their lives with their other three sons and four daughters, always remembering you but aware there was a possibility you had somehow killed yourself. In this lifetime, the Englishman became your father, his children became your cousins, your mother became your guardian godmother, who was brought into your life to take care of you, and your father of the past lifetime has moved on in the spirit plane. That is that and that is that.'

'That is that and that is that means? You have shown me a trailer and now you say that is that, that too not once but twice: that is that. Strange Guru you are, dear Baba! Will you please tell me then what happened?'

'I made a mistake getting you to this cave of mine. There was so much peace out here.'

'My dream, my rules, Baba. Please elaborate, O chain-smoking Master of all Universes.'

Then Baba began to abuse in various languages. It is best to not write all that down. Not for any reason, but that normal devotees do not expect their God to use the most foul words and abuse.

'What I am going to do is give you the ability to go into the past and come back to the present as and when you want. So you can visit the time when you were the nineteen-year-old lad who spent time with me, but as a spirit body, and also come back to the cave and spend time with me as a fifty-four-year-old demented goat.'

'You are not going to send me anywhere alone, Baba. You please remove another spark from Your body and come along with me. I am not going anywhere without You.'

'Allah, Allah, Allah, if there is anybody who can make spirituality seem like a bad lifestyle decision, then, my son, it is bloody you. Come on!'

And in the next instant Baba and Rabda found themselves in Shirdi; it was the year 1858. Baba Sai had returned to Shirdi nearly three and a half years after He first stepped foot in the Holy Land. Not many are really aware of where Baba Sai disappeared to for those almost-four years before He returned to stay in Shirdi for the next sixty years where He took samadhi in October 1918.

Rabda knew it was 1858. How, he was not sure. He was just made aware. Baba Sai was with him. Though Rabda knew Baba Sai was still in the cave, Baba Sai was with him here too, as even now Baba Sai was muttering and abusing under His breath.

> Every time you serve a Master or give a Master what
> He or She asks for, the Master has to repay it ten- or
> hundredfold more. If you love your Master, He or She
> will love you a thousandfold more.

So Rabda saw Baba enter Shirdi, with pomp and music as if the cosmos was well aware of the magnitude of Baba's arrival in Shirdi, though all around people were engrossed in the wedding celebration in which Baba was a guest. He was a young man. Difficult to ascertain His age. He looked twenty-two but could have been twenty-seven. Caiz was aware of the story of how Baba had helped Chand Patil find his horse that had strayed away for days and was not to be found. Chand Patil saw this fakir sitting under a tree. The fakir smiled and called him by his name and told him to come relax, have a smoke, and that his horse was not lost but grazing by the river.

Chand Patil was wonderstruck by how this fakir knew his name, and how on earth did he manage to get from within the earth burning hot coal to light his chillum? He sat down, completely in awe of this young fakir and for a while forgot all about his horse and both the men smoked. Suddenly Chand Patil remembered, with the reassurance of the young fakir, that the horse was stuffing its face by the river. Chand ran towards the gush of water, and to his surprise he found the four-footed idiot busy chomping away.

Chand Patil invited Baba to be part of the wedding procession which was taking place in Shirdi and this is how Baba entered Shirdi, though not for the first time. He had arrived in Shirdi some time back and He left as suddenly as He had arrived. Now after years He was entering Shirdi, with all the pomp and honour meant for the dignitaries.

Baba halted in front of Lord Khandoba's temple. Caiz observed that Baba was around five feet six inches tall. His skin colour was golden yellow; He was not fair or dark skinned. He was neither thin nor fat. His eyes, Caiz realized, changed colours with what was going on within Him. The village priest, Mahalsapati, came out of the temple, and halted. He seemed mesmerized by this young fakir.

Mahalsapati was an orthodox Hindu priest. Generations of communal prejudices had moulded him into a good human being who was wary of Muslims and though he communicated with them, he kept his distance if it was possible. But one look at this fakir and Mahalsapati felt as though somebody had ripped open his heart and now it throbbed with a new sensation. He was not certain what it was and Caiz realized that the poor man was confused about all that which went on within him. He approached Baba who looked at the priest with amused tenderness. The young fakir was already on his way to self-realization but still not completely there. Caiz was certain that Baba Sai was extremely evolved at that time but still had not reached the state of complete Oneness with the One.

Mahalsapati folded his hands, did a namaste, which

meant 'I bow to the God within You' and said the most famous words ever spoken in any language ever: 'Ya Sai'.

Caiz looked at Baba Sai standing with him, watching all the goings-on like in a movie.

'You look very handsome I must say, Baba, but why the word Sai? Why not some other name?'

Baba Sai turned towards Caiz.

'Halkat, all fakirs, dervishes, Sufis those days were called Sai. In reality it is *saih,* which is a Persian word to address all men of God, thus Mahalsa had not invented the name. In Persian, every dervish was called Saih, and eventually people referred to me only as Sai.'

'Ooooooo. You are so knowledgeable Mr Saih, but do not disturb, let us now watch the movie in peace. You won't be having any popcorn, right? Right.'

Caiz heard Baba muttering very inventive abuses and he smiled. He loved the grumpy Old Man.

So Mahalsapati did a namaste and said 'Ya Sai'. *Ya,* in Marathi, means 'come' or 'welcome'. But Caiz could see the confusion in the eyes and heart of the priest. The reason why Baba stopped next to Lord Khandoba's temple was that in those days Lord Khandoba was accepted by both Hindus and Muslims as an Energy of God.

In earlier centuries, Lord Khandoba was worshipped in many temples as Lord Subramaniya, the son of Lord Shiva and Ma Parvati. But he is now considered to be the avatar of Lord Shiva, looks like a Pathan on horseback, and has a custodian who is a Muslim lady.

So Baba Sai had halted in front of Lord Khandoba's temple, thinking that this was the place He would rest.

Mahalsapati now was in a jam. In Shirdi, Lord Khandoba's temple was meant only for Hindus. He felt an inexplicable pull towards the young fakir but the fakir was obviously a Muslim and he could not enter Lord Khandoba's temple and that was that.

Baba Sai realized that the manner in which Mahalsapati greeted Him without ushering Him into the temple meant Baba had to walk away.

'Baba, Mahalsapati wants you in the temple but can't tell you to come in. Why?'

'Bachcha, if there is anything I have learnt, it is that even my sixty-odd years of living in Shirdi could not change the mindset and prejudices of people. All my life as Sai Baba of Shirdi, I preached Oneness. I did not reveal my name, my religion, my past, anything. I on purpose kept my birth a secret and though there is a lot of speculation, none is true. Nobody but the Oneness Family knows about my origins and that is the way it is meant to be. All through my stay in Shirdi, I would tell one and all, "Sab ka Malik ek", which you know means that the Lord of all is One. But did anybody truly want the One? No. They wanted their worldly wishes to be granted and Baba can take His Oneness and go boil His head. The moment I dropped my body, Hindus and Muslims began their chutiyagiri and shaitanpana. Thus if you ask me, Rabda, your Baba Sai failed.'

Caiz nodded. He could do little but nod. It was a fact. We, the mankind species, are either the scum of creation or the Radiance of the One. Unfortunately, the former applies to most of us, he realized.

So Mahalsapati—though in his heart he wanted to embrace

Baba Sai, the young fakir—eventually had to, without saying a word, refuse Baba refuge in Lord Khandoba's temple.

Baba Sai was dressed in a typical fakir dress code. He had long hair that reached way below His back. He wore a green cap and though He wore a loose white shirt and a dhoti, there was a green shawl draped over His shoulders. Baba Sai smiled and then left the celebrations and wandered into the forest.

Caiz then saw Baba sitting under various trees, deep in meditation. He spent days and nights in this state, irrespective of the weather or the hardship. For the first few weeks, He would, when not meditating, wander all around Shirdi and in the nearby villages. Children thought Him mad as often He would speak with Himself and sometimes laugh and sometimes curse. Kids, who by nature are innocent and extremely cruel, would taunt Him and even throw stones at Him and, Baba, depending on His mood, would either indulge them or scare them shitless and throw stones right back at them.

This is where a young boy called Lal came into the picture. Whenever he could, he would fight with the boys to leave Baba Sai alone. Very often he would throw stones back at the boys who tried to trouble Baba. Baba Sai would see him and smile. The young Lal, who was then called Rabda, would smile back. He could not be seen spending time with the fakir, as his family were staunch Hindus and did not associate themselves with Muslims or fakirs. But Lal, who was ten years old or so, did all he could to help Baba be in peace when He meditated.

Mahalsapati was in turmoil. Every time he saw Baba, he

was certain this was no ordinary fakir and that this Fakir was his Guru. But he was a traditional Hindu priest. How could he go about making a fakir his Guru? But he spoke with great respect of this young fakir and eventually he began to meet Baba Sai when Baba would wander the roads of Shirdi. Even then Baba called him Bhagat, which means a disciple, a follower, a devotee.

Now Mahalsapati had two friends, Kasinath, who was the village tailor, and another called Joge, and these three men began to spend time with Baba and offer Him food, tobacco, a rag cloth which Baba used on and off for sitting or sleeping on under the trees. Baba loved the margosa or neem trees and He was usually found meditating under them. So the relationship between Mahalsapati and Baba began to grow. In a short time Mahalsapati was convinced that Baba was his Guru and in reality he was Baba's first disciple. He began to treat Baba as God incarnate long before the world acknowledged Baba's Godhood, when for the world He was a simple fakir—or a mad, abusive, powerful fakir.

A few months passed, and a lady by the name of Bayaja, later known as Bayaja Ma, married a very rich landowner called Ganapath Kote Patil. The moment Bayaja saw Baba, she knew He was the One. Bayaja's philosophy was simple. Food was God. To feed the poor and the sages and the fakirs was as spiritual as sitting in prayers and meditation.

'Isn't she the same lady who searched far and wide to feed You, Baba, and her son, called Tatya, was one of Your favourites, and it is said that You gave Your life up to save Tatya's life?'

'Yes, Bayaja Ma loved me like her father, brother and son.

Our relationship went back many lifetimes to when she was a sister of mine in a birth. *Religion is transient as when you take another birth, your religion might change, but spiritual love and selfless love is permanent. They remain life after life after life.* Shaitan, just see what is being shown to you, halkat, how much you disturb me.'

'A strange God You are! Everybody thinks You are so polite and like a normal God and Master, like a grandfather, but the moment You open Your mouth, instead of mantras, I get to hear all this . . .'

'See.'

So Caiz looked. Now Bayaja Ma took it upon herself to take care of Baba Sai. Baba spent most of His time in the babul forest under a neem tree. But very often He would disappear and then be found someplace else, far away from the prying eyes of anybody. The forest was vast and wide and there was no proper pathway. But Bayaja would wake up, have a bath, say her prayers, prepare her food, and then pack food for Baba, and then go in search of Him. She sometimes would find Him in a short while or sometimes would take a really long time. But she was clear that till she fed Baba, she would not eat a morsel of food or drink water.

Very often Lal, or the young Rabda, would help Bayaja by first locating Baba and then running to inform Bayaja where Baba was seated. But more often than not, Lal would be in school when all this took place and thus Bayaja had to walk miles sometimes to find Baba, traverse bushes and thorns, then feed Him and return home to partake of food and water.

'She really served me when I was still walking the path like any other seeker. She served me, though I looked like a fakir and thus was considered a Muslim, and did not care what anybody said or thought. Every day, for the over two and a half years that I spent in the forest and in the wilderness, every day she would walk to wherever I was, and make sure I ate. Often I would be deep in meditation and she would, like a mother feeding her infant child, slowly make me eat food. She would actually open my mouth, feed me, cajole me, so that eventually I would eat and then open my eyes, and when she was sure I would eat the food, she would go back to her home and take care of her duties.'

And Caiz saw it all. The way she carried the basket with food and water, walked and called out to Baba and then found Him, and if He was aware of His surroundings, she would lay the banana leaf, spread the food, and then when Baba put a morsel in His mouth, only then would she leave. Or if He was in meditation, she would make small morsels of food and slowly feed Him; often Baba would remain in meditation but she would make sure He had eaten and then leave.

Often Rabda would be with Bayaja and sit and see all of this. Baba would say something and the boy would laugh aloud. Frequently Bayaja's son, Tatya, too would accompany his mother and Baba was always cheerful and kind with children. Tatya would climb on to Baba's shoulder and play and scream and Baba would chuckle and smile and indulge the children. He would not like anybody hitting a child, and that was the case from the very beginning. Yes, He was clear that children are not the friends of parents. Do not become a friend of your child because if you too become friends then who will play the role of a parent? But treat children with compassion and love as they are what parents make them.

Baba had now begun to wear a white robe and tie a white cloth over His head. The image that we have in our minds started within a few months of Baba living in Shirdi. He realized that He was neither a Hindu nor a Muslim, thus He chose the colour white, which stands for purity, humility and Oneness.

The decision to insist on Baba staying in the dilapidated masjid came after nearly two and a half years of Baba living in the forest. All this while the people of Shirdi had slowly begun to accept Baba as their own, but most of them still thought He was a mad fakir. A number of people would come to Baba for a cure for something or the other. Baba would give them some leaves, some mixture, or some remedy to be concocted at home and they would sometimes give Him some food or tobacco and very often give Him nothing and He did not care what was given or said. He went about in the world, but was not part of it.

Caiz saw it rain. It was pouring. He saw Mahalsapati and his two friends running hither and thither trying to locate Baba. It was pouring so heavily that after a while they could go nowhere. The situation was so bad that nobody could venture out of the house. Bayaja Ma too could not leave the house and not many people know that she for those two days did not have water or food. This was because as she had not been able to feed Baba as she could not find Him and also after a while it was impossible to venture out. When the rain stopped, they found Baba still under the margosa tree, half sitting, half reclining, in a state of complete meditation, with all the filth of the village and forest clinging to Him, but He was oblivious. Nobody dared touch Him as He was not known to tolerate fools and known for a quick temper, abusive language and was not beyond thrashing people witless.

After a few hours, Caiz saw Baba coming back to normal consciousness. Mahalsapati bowed down to Baba and told Him that henceforth He would live in the masjid, as He was not just a man of God—He was no longer the guest of the village but one of them and was Mahalsapati's father, brother, friend and Guru.

Baba looked around and saw Bayaja Ma crying silently in a corner. He saw the kids, some shocked at how He could have survived the storm and the flood and everything. He nodded His head and slowly walked towards the masjid, a broken-down house made out of mud and cow dung, not more than ten feet long and seven feet deep and with the east side open to the forces of nature. Baba looked at the masjid and smiled.

'My Mother at last has opened Her arms to Me. This is no longer a masjid. This is Masjid Mai, the Mother of all Mothers.'

So Baba Sai began to live in Dwarka Mai or Masjid Ayi, as Baba often referred to His most humble dwelling. Life became simpler for Bayaja Ma after that as Sai began to go to five houses to, as He would say, beg for love. He barely slept at night. He would be deep in meditation. Initially, He would heal through herbs but once He lit the Holy Fire Mother, Dhuni Mai, He would only give the Holy Ash for all purposes. Caiz realized that for the next thirty years, apart from folks in Shirdi and nearby villages, nobody really knew of Baba Sai. Yes, slowly a number of Sufis would come and spend time with Baba and Baba would help them on their spiritual path.

During those days there were two highly evolved spiritual personalities living in Shirdi, Jankidas and Devidas.

Baba used to spend time with both of them. Devidas had arrived before Baba and was considered a much-evolved soul. Baba and Devidas would sit in Lord Hanuman's temple and often spend hours talking to each other. They loved each other, which was obvious by the respect they accorded to each other.

Jankidas came later but he was extremely close to Baba and would often come and spend time with Baba in Dwarka Mai and often Baba would go find Jankidas, wherever He was meditating and then they would spend time with each other.

Caiz realized that jealousy exists amongst maggots. Giants are never jealous of each other. Baba Sai would venture to the neighbouring villages and, especially when He went to Rahata, He would bring back various saplings, mainly marigold and jasmine, and plant them wherever He deemed fit and then tenderly nurture them, talk to them, even caress them, often cajole them to grow and blossom out, revealing the glory of God. Baba began to cultivate a garden, which sixty years later would be overlooking His own physical remains. Caiz realized that, for three years, Baba's main work in Shirdi was to plant saplings and see them blossom and grow.

Every day Baba would go and beg for His food and wherever Bayaja Ma was, she would leave everything and rush to serve her Sai food. Sometimes Baba would go as many as fifteen times to her house to beg for food and Bayaja Ma would, each time, leave everything and greet Sai as though she was seeing Him after months. Tatya, her son, was very close to Baba and he began to spend, along with Mahalsapati, time with Baba. In fact after a few years, Mahalsapati and Tatya would sleep with Baba in Dwarka Mai.

No matter what, Baba was still considered a Muslim and by many a mad fakir. This was understandable, as Baba was in a state of God-intoxication. When the moment seized Him, He was lost to His surroundings and He would begin to talk to what seemed Himself, whereas Caiz realized that He was talking to other spirits around Him, instructing them about their duties. Caiz saw Rabda come to Baba Sai as a spirit and Baba Sai embrace Rabda. After that Rabda was where Sai was along with other spirit agents or abdals, who would frequent Baba for spiritual growth and work duties, to serve, guide, protect, help people living in the breadth and depth of the world. Nobody could see all this and thus Baba was considered mad. He never bothered telling anybody why He did what He did. Yes, He abused and thrashed people nice and proper regularly and slowly it was known by one and all that He was a rare gem, to be nurtured and understood, but the fact remained that most people thought Baba was batty as a lamp post.

Baba loved to wrestle and would wrestle often but most of all He loved to sing and dance. There was a place for Muslim travellers, a kind of a rest house called Takia, and Baba would often spend time there at night, singing and dancing amongst other Sufis and devotees. He would tie small tinkling ornaments or trinkets, ghungroos, around His ankles and dance and sing. Most of His songs were in Persian or Arabic or those of the poet and master Kabir.

Baba loved to help people and those in need. If he found that there was nobody to take care of an ailing person, Baba would sit by the ailing person, often through the night, always in prayer, chanting, chanting, chanting, nursing the sick person, never charging any money, never expecting anything, always wanting to bring people out of darkness into the Light.

All through, Baba did not talk much, did not sleep much, did not eat much. Yes, He was made fun of, the children would trouble Him, the vendors would often ridicule Him for asking for oil to burn His beloved oil lamps and Baba would, depending upon His state of being, smile, ignore, abuse or thrash. And He was strong.

Shama entered Baba's life then. He was a schoolteacher who did not think much of Baba but at night He would hear Baba slowly talk in various languages to nobody in particular. Shama lived close to Dwarka Mai and could hear Baba converse in various languages. This brought about an interest in his heart and in not much time Shama and Baba were bosom friends. Shama loved Baba but spoke to Him as a friend. Often he would speak as though Baba was not Sai but just Shama's friend, and Baba would never take offence.

Baba was humility personified. Once a Muslim fakir came and lived with Baba and after a while took Baba with him to another village, where Baba was made to serve this man. Shirdi villagers were saddened and aghast at how Baba was, without any ego, serving that strange man. It was then that Devidas and Jankidas came into the scene and in an argument destroyed the false notion the so-called Sufi had about himself and brought Baba back to Shirdi. It did not matter to Baba what people considered Him to be. It did not matter if people ridiculed Him or thought Him mad. It did not matter whether He had to serve somebody else, as the only thing that mattered to Baba, Caiz realized, was that He was one with the Creator. With 'Allah Malik' on His lips, in His heart, the very sigh of His soul, nothing mattered to Baba but constant communion with the One.

The stream of true Sufis and seekers kept coming to Baba but Caiz realized that, unfortunately, nobody was there to keep an account of what transpired. Also Abdul was still to come. Shirdi was a beautiful but a small village. Life was serene. Though India was under the rule of the British, in Shirdi, it mattered squat. People were busy in their farming and in their rituals and in their prejudices and in their trying to keep body and soul together.

Baba's routine very rarely changed. Baba hated change in routine or any kind of change. That is why He used to go to only those five houses to beg for food. His schedule was like clockwork till He took samadhi but He was most liberal. He hated any kind of orthodox behaviour. Yes, He loved spiritual living but not an orthodox or fanatical mindset. He didn't care much about what people thought about Him, so when Muslims thought He was a Muslim, He wouldn't go out of His way to prove them wrong and so with the Hindus. Eventually everybody came to one conclusion: that whoever He was, whether sane or insane, was still out in the open up for debate, but that Baba Sai loved the One, and money, power, women, food, status, comfort, climate . . . nothing, just nothing mattered to Him. He was a king who was not attached to His kingdom but only to the firm belief of helping all those who came to Him in need.

The role of the Master is to help each child go through
their lot and their karma and the experiences with
calmness, wisdom, courage and positive acceptance.

They were back in the cave. No matter where Caiz was,
it was the cave that made him feel most at home. He
felt as though he had Baba Sai to himself, though the
countless sparks flying into Baba, emitting from Baba and
leaving the cave left Caiz in no doubt that Baba was with
whosoever really called out to Him.

'Baba, there are so many who are going through hell. The
Hindus believe that there are thirty-three crore Gods and
Goddesses and there are so many Masters. I mean there are
more Gods in heaven than there are people in a few countries
down here on Mother Earth. Why can't you all just work
something out and tell those going through their private hell?'

'You are such a classical idiot, my daft child. The answer
is simple, Rabda. Either you believe that God does not exist,
there is no Supreme Power running this grand show, or you
believe in a just God. You cannot believe in a God who exists
but is unjust. God is completely just. S(H)e loves each and
every being, no matter how seemingly insignificant it may
be to others. God exists and throbs in a worm just as S(H)e
breathes and works through a perfect Master and archangels.

The truth of life is that in each being exists the One, but in human beings, the ability to realize and become one with the Almighty can be realized the fastest and easiest. That is why it is said that mankind was created in the image of the Lord and even angels used to bow down to mankind. The true image of mankind is a throbbing God waiting to be realized. Mankind is a vault where the One resides but most often is buried under the illusions, desires, reactions and past experiences. Thus, though God exists in each one of us, S(H)e is so bloody well hidden that lifetimes go by before one first realizes that God exists within the individual and then another few lifetimes go by in just clearing the clutter.

'To blame God and Master for being unjust is like going to a restaurant, eating to your heart's content, drinking till your liver begins to protest but when the bill comes, the time to pay for what you have eaten, drunk and indulged in, you start saying that the restaurant is mean, unfair, unjust, and why are you forced to pay, and why is this amount to be paid far greater than that for the people seated on the other table. The people seated on the other table may have had simple food and thus the final bill is far less than the former one, but imagine the individual grumbling and fighting and cussing, saying that the owner is unfair. Where has the owner come into the picture? You went to a restaurant. You knew the price of each thing you ate and drank. You enjoyed yourself. And now the bill has come. Pay up quietly. Nobody but you has to pay for it as you have indulged yourself till your stomach seems to burst and your liver wants to pack up. To call the cook, waiter, cashier and the owner mean, unjust and partial makes no sense. And you can create all the ruckus you want, but you will have to pay the bill. This is the eternal law, Rabda. It is applicable to every being. Even Gods are not exempt from this law.

'Look at Lord Rama's life. He is the Vishnu Avatar. Due to a curse incurred by Lord Vishnu, he had to come down in the physical body and go through certain experiences. He came down as Lord Rama. What a life Lord Rama had! First of all he is not aware that he is an avatar. He is sent to exile for fourteen years. Ravana kidnaps Ma Sita and spends the entire exile with Ma Sita. Lord Rama wages a war and eventually gets Ma back but in a few months, to maintain peace and harmony amongst those he reigns over, he has no option but to tell Ma to go away. She goes away and he spends much more than a decade without Ma and his twin sons. Eventually due again to strained conditions where his own sons Luv and Kush wage a war against their own father's army, the father and sons meet. Once again, Lord Rama has to ask Ma Sita to prove herself and she, heartbroken, calls out to Mother Earth to open up and devour her. This is what happens. So Lord Rama meets his beloved to lose her again, for ever. He takes his sons with him and after making sure they are capable of handling life on their own, he does jal samadhi, which means he walks into the ocean never to come back.'

'You mean Lord Rama committed suicide?'

'In modern-day parlance, yes, you could say Lord Rama committed suicide.'

'Then I am in illustrious company, what say, Baba?'

Baba chose the most abusive words but there was only love in His eyes.

'So what Lord Rama's story tries to tell one and all is that nobody escapes karma and its laws. Lord Jesus took on the karmic load of all creation. His crucifixion broke heaven's heart. If They, God-manifest, can go through such suffering, why should you and I cry about our lot!'

'It is not as easy as You say, Baba. You and Lord Rama and Lord Jesus are God incarnates. We are normal human beings surrounded by chutiyas and our own fucking idiosyncrasies. Each one wants to slander the other. Each one wants to pull the other down. Each one wants to take the other's rightful share. Life is not that easy, Baba, for folks like us.'

'You bloody idiot, I am telling you God resides in each one. You need to dive within to reach the pearl. Who said that was easy? But you need to keep at it, bachcha. In every situation which is not pleasant, each individual usually has three alternatives to handle the situation. The first is you give your best to the problem or situation, and you give it for a proper duration of time and then if the situation does not change, you have the right to walk out or distance yourself from the situation. But many times one cannot walk away from a situation. It could be a bad marriage and children involved or the fear of starting afresh or having nobody to fall back on or it could be at a job, where the employer might be trying to nail your family jewels to the floor or is very manipulative or the colleagues are political or whatever, or it could be with parents or siblings. It could be with some work initiated which needs to be either continued or dissolved. So if after giving your best, the situation does not change and you cannot walk away, then you are left with two alternatives. The first alternative is as you cannot move away and the situation is not going to improve or change, you need to make peace with the situation and try to live a life with positive acceptance, calmness, without reacting, trying to find peace and happiness and being happy with small mercies, as you truly have no other option. You cannot walk away, so you might as well make the most of the situation and try to find happiness and peace and self-respect within yourself and in the narrow by-lanes of the situation.

'The other alternative is to stew and fret and fume and fight and slander and gossip and behave like a disgruntled animal or play the victim and gain the sympathy of one and all, thus making the karma get knotted only further and increase in intensity. The choice is yours and one has to make this choice over and over and over again. In a day this choice might have to be made ten times. Imagine you start moving towards a place of finding peace in your lot and accepting whatever is in store with dignified calmness and fortitude and courage. This is where free will in the right manner comes across. Karma has put you in an uncomfortable situation but now do you want to live in peace or create further hell for yourself and those around you? So do you want to use your free will to experience the hardship or situation, and get done with it and grow spiritually with it, using the karmic experience as a springboard to move higher spiritually and deeper within? Or do you want to create more karma by going through the situation like a bloody camel that has had chilli powder sprayed into its eyes and shoved up its arse?

'So all is not destined. Most may be but each individual has a certain percentage as free will. The higher you grow spiritually the greater is the free will you will have in your grasp. And if all is destined then how does mankind create more karma or obliterate the pending karma? Yes, there are certain milestones in the karmic blueprint which each individual will have to experience but even the process of how to go through the experience depends on one's use of free will. Let us say, an accident or hardship is destined. But how one goes through the accident and the recovery or the maiming process, how one goes through the hardship and ordeal, depends upon one's use of free will, which will further create more karma—either the karma that liberates or the karma that suffocates and cages. Thus even if one has ten per cent as free will and all else as karmic experiences of give and take, that ten per cent is more important as it is that ten per cent which is going to decide your future lifetimes, your evolvement, your being liberated or encaged. So use your free will very well.'

'So You mean each individual is the architect of his or her own destiny?'

'Obviously. You sow as you reap. Where do God and Master come between all this? We will always be with you when you call out to us. Also pray for the right things. If you have to experience something, it is a milestone in your karmic blueprint, then pray that your Lord, Goddess, Master bless you to go through the experience with calmness, peace, courage, joy, peaceful surrender and acceptance.

'Rabda, if you read about me and my life, you will notice that those who were closest to me had to face so many hardships and so much heartbreak. They were living with me in Shirdi. I was in the body. I was there with them. They used to meet me every day, sometimes many times in a day.

But they had to go through their suffering and karma, beta. Could I save them from their destiny? Yes, I could have postponed the inevitable but what one sows one reaps. My closest disciples lost their children at a young age. They became bankrupt.

'RadhaKrishna Ayi, whom I used to call RadhaKrishni or Ayi, which means mother, or Sala, as when she came to Shirdi, she had been roaming from one pilgrimage place to another for five years, all alone, and there was a broken-down school in which I told her to go and reside and she made it her home. What was her life? She was married at the age of seventeen and a week later her husband passed away and it broke her emotionally and mentally. But from the moment she came to Shirdi, I became her presiding Lord and Master and she served me for nearly ten years. She obeyed me and I was very strict with her as I needed to erase her karmic blueprint or else she would have lifetimes of suffering. She served me and did exactly as I told her to and, Rabda, how do you think she died? She got burnt alive. A lot of people think she committed suicide but she got burnt alive. Not more than hundred feet from where I sat. The Sai sat in Dwarka Mai, and she got burnt alive. She served me day and night. She used to sweep the roads I walked on so that pebbles and stones would not hurt my feet and cow dung and dog shit would not soil my clothes or my feet. She would take care of all those I sent to her house, feed them, nurture them and eat only the simple roti and some vegetable I sent for her. She would only eat my leftovers though she cooked for countless who came to meet me. She was not even allowed to come inside the masjid. I have screamed and abused her for making changes in Dwarka Mai and Chavadi but she would silently go through the screaming and ranting and abuses, and do all that so I would be at peace. When I would rest in Chavadi every alternate night, she would often at night clean the masjid walls as soot would accumulate from the ever-burning Fire, Dhuni Mai. She would clean the whole masjid, and then keep everything back as it was so that I would not get angry at anything being touched. In fact so many rituals connected with me are due to Ayi's insistence and persistence. The pomp and glory with which I am worshipped today and was worshipped when I was in the body is due to RadhaKrishni. She wanted me to be worshipped like a king, like Lord Vithal, who is the king of Pandharpur.

'First the Urus began and then later on it was decided to merge the Urus celebration with the festival of Ram Navami. For me it was done to bring about harmony amongst my Hindu and Muslim children. Earlier, seven thousand people would gather and eventually it went up to seventy thousand devotees. Sala Ayi was in charge of all the internal arrangements. From the needs of the pilgrims to getting the paraphernalia ready for the festival, all she did on her own. The cooking was done by her and the ginger-powder-and-sugar prasad, which till date devotees are given in Shirdi, was first prepared by RadhaKrishni.

'I would sleep every alternate night at Chavadi, and the whole procession taking me from Dwarka Mai to Chavadi, with pomp and glory and music and dancing, like a king travelling from one country to another, was started and supervised by her. I would want to eat something and tell my people to inform RadhaKrishni about the dishes and,

Rabda, she would have already prepared those very dishes. She loved me so much that she even knew what I would like to eat, as and when I desired to eat something. She loved to sing and her voice was so melodious you felt the Gods had descended to hear her. She loved singing songs of Sant Tukaram and Jaydev. She loved to take her ektara, the one-stringed instrument, and sing, and I could hear her sing those divine words. So many times I have sat and heard her sing from far. Yes, she had a temper and could be blunt and also very emotional and erratic in nature but nobody could love me the way she did. She truly did not want anything from me. She just wanted to love and worship me.

'Her life was spent thinking about and loving me and I had to let her die by being burnt to death. Do you have any idea what it is to have one's child burnt to death, and when you can stop it, but you know it is best for the child to go through the experience so that the child is freed from the mundane existence of maya and can progress on a spiritual path, either again in the body or in the spirit? So many could not understand how Sai could let RadhaKrishni die in such a brutal manner but the Fakir knows and the Fakir knows the best for all. The ways and workings of the Masters are unfathomable. Yes, every time you serve a Master or give a Master what He or She asks for, the Master has to repay it ten- or hundredfold more. If you love your Master, He or She will love you a thousandfold more. This is how we operate. We never leave a debt unpaid or unrewarded. We are not looking for praise or adulation. Our role is to first help you get rid of the karmic baggage by making you go deeper within and finding your God and Master within. If you have to go through the worst ordeal or life or pass over, so be it, go through it knowing we go through it too with you, but be certain it is for your well-being and perpetual salvation. Never ever doubt this. I did not let Ayi burn. I made sure all her pending karma was burnt away and she merged with me. Even now she serves me in more ways than anybody can fathom but, Rabda, karma had to be burnt away, bachcha. This is the law. This is the way. This is how it is meant to be.'

The more selfless your love, the greater the happiness all around.

Baba and Rabda sat in silence. Baba had told him often that all of heaven and beyond reposes in the womb of calm silence. Very often Baba would shut His eyes and go within and the power and intensity of His aura would increase. It was strange that even when Rabda sat in silence, sometimes looking out into the sky or at the snow-capped mountains or the Fire, or just observing Baba, with no ripple in his mind, no break in his breathing, no conflict in his heart, no words floating within or without, he felt a sense of Oneness with Baba, the world around and the beyond the beyond. But there was one thought bothering him, that one pathanikidda, or large worm, wriggling about in his auric rectal opening.

'Speak up, Rabda, as, remember, silence when calm can bring the very Gods to the chambers of your heart and your surroundings but silent anger attracts lower energies to the person as it creates spots and then holes in the aura and distorts the vibrations in the surroundings. And confused silence is just a nuisance and you, my boy, are so confused and silent that they should create another word for your quiet imbecility.'

'I guess you can tell me anything as you have God and the entire army of Light Workers at Your call and You are my God and I am just a musician . . .'

'A very off-tune musician, I may add, and one who can't even commit suicide silently, just in case you want to get into the heart of the matter . . .'

'Hilarious, but as You wanted to know what I wanted to say, here goes. Remember You told me about how karma has to be faced up to and how what one goes through one *has* to go through? You spoke about RadhaKrishna Ayi and how You sat not a hundred feet away, knowing she was burning to death, and still could not or would not save her. Though You could, You still did not, obviously for her future life and karmic growth and all the shit-shat that spirituality so beautifully words . . . spirituality can truly word everything so beautifully and convincingly . . . but Your life is filled with miracles. Left, right and centre You used to perform miracles. You have saved people from death so very often. You, just to make Your devotees reach the railway station and catch the train on time, have ordered the sky to stop raining and the sky has obliged. You have made the fire calm down, sitting in the masjid, while the fire would have burnt Your devotees' crops down. You have made the blind see, the dead alive, the barren get children . . .'

'Obviously I have no mantra or power to shut you up, now that would be a miracle . . .'

'And you have shocked people witless by separating Your limbs all over the Masjid Ayi or Dwarka Mai, and then sort of saying, "This is yoga, do not give too much attention to my limbs scattered all over the place." You have done it all. You are one of the only Masters who is never shy of performing a damn miracle. You read the minds and hearts of everybody who came in front of you. You knew exactly what each one said or did. You with Your touch could grant a glimpse of the very creation, but still You sat and allowed one of Your greatest disciples to burn to death. You allowed Your nearest and dearest devotees, who served You and spent so much time and their very lives with you, to suffer. Their small children would die and You would do nothing. They would become bankrupt and You would give your karma monologue. Why? If You do something and can do something, do so for all, or do not do it for anybody. Why make some feel special and others feel alone and unloved?'

Baba filled the chillum and smoked and then passed it on to Rabda. This way both the men smoked for a while. Baba's face glowed. His eyes radiated all of divinity. He then looked at Rabda and smiled.

'How much you talk, bachcha?' Then He smiled and shut His eyes. It was as though this seemingly glaring paradox had bothered Him too.

'I will tell you exactly the same words which I told my dear Nana Saheb . . .'

'The same chap for whom you materialized a horse carriage and a driver so that the Udhi, Holy Ash, you had given for Nana's daughter, who was in labour in another town, but in severe pain and in danger of dying, could receive in the middle of the night? You sent somebody carrying the Udhi . . .'

'Ramgir Bua . . .'

'Okay, so You sent Ramgir to give Nana the Holy Ash

and our man Ramgir gets off the train, and a horse carriage, with a driver, materializes, takes Ramgir to Nana's house, and when Nana gets the Udhi and asks Ramgir how he had come so late in the night, so far away from the station. Ramgir says by the horse carriage he, Nana, had sent and Nana says, what the . . . and Ramgir looks around and there is no horse carriage, no horse crapping its arse out, no driver and Ramgir says, scratch my swollen balls.'

'Yes, the same Nana. Now can I continue speaking or are you going to further show off your knowledge of how much you know of my life?'

'Okay, go on. Some other Master would have been beaming from ear to toe and blessing me with all sorts of stuff for being so informed about all Their spiritual showing-off.'

'My bachcha, this world loves glitter. They love it. They love tamasha, dramatics. Stop the rain, get the blind to see, walk on water, read their minds, predict the future, they love all this and come from far and wide, and more the miracles the greater the Master. You have to keep performing like a dancer or a clown in the circus, keep performing miracles like a juggler and only then one can win the faith and love of a few. No miracles means the Master is a bloody sham or a chutiya and a waste of time.

'Tajuddin Baba and I performed miracles as that was our portfolio. He and I performed miracles at the drop of a hat, as the ones who came to us were so poor, so broken, so flogged that they needed to go beyond the state of hopelessness and be embraced with the grace of the Master, in this case through miracles. Some Masters have to perform miracles while some have to make sure They refrain from obvious miracles, though the moment you come into contact with a Master, miracles abound—some you can see and some you will never see or even know about till much later.

'Do you know what the greatest miracle is? Leading an individual from darkness into Light is the greatest miracle, as everything noble and good begins when an individual starts embracing the Divine Light and walks on the path of radiance. The miracle takes place each moment of your life then as the Light slowly burns away the lifetimes and scores of karmic build-up and baggage. When a Master predicts something, that prediction is momentary. For a particular reason or purpose. *But when a Master initiates you into the path of radiance, when a Master takes you away from darkness into His Light, that miracle is for ever and evermore. But how many want such a miracle? They want pomp, dance, song and drama.*

'What I told Nana Saheb over a hundred years ago still applies to me and all the Masters. Shut your mouth, Rabda, you look very funny.'

'Off, for the Lord of God will you get going *Babae*.'

'This is what I said.'

And suddenly Rabda was in Shirdi. He was in Dwarka Mai. Baba was in the flesh, as Sai Baba of Shirdi. He saw Nana Saheb. Both of them were seated alone near the Holy Fire, Dhuni Mai. And Baba said, 'I will not allow my devotees to come to harm. If a devotee is about to fall, I stretch my hands and instead of two, with four outstretched hands I support my devotee. I will not let my child fall.'

Rabda saw Nana nod and then Nana said nobody had to fear as Baba was the God of miracles and Rabda saw Baba smile but it was a sad smile, a smile where His eyes did not twinkle but went deeper within.

Then Baba spoke softly.

'No, Nana, I do not perform any miracles. You have village astrologers. They work two or four days ahead of time and give out their predictions. Some of them come true. I look further ahead. My art is also a sort of astrology. But you people do not understand this. To you, my words look like magic, a chamatkar, because you do not know the future. So you regard events as proofs of miracle-working power and you turn your reverence on to me. I, on my part, turn your reverence on to God and see that you are really benefited.'

Slowly the image began to fade and Rabda was back in the cave along with Baba and the holy Fire.

'How the hell did You manage this flashback?'

'You have grown up on such badly made films so I thought you would like the zoom-in and zoom-out black-and-white flashback.'

'Yes, but why was everything in black and white?'

'Early Hindi movie flashbacks were in black and white so just for effect, bachcha.'

'You are a very funny God, Baba.'

'Oh that I am, you worm of mine. So understand a few things clearly. The Master's role in the life of a devotee or a disciple is not to change and manipulate the karmic blueprint. The role of the Master is to help each child go through their lot and their karma and the experiences with calmness, wisdom, courage and positive acceptance. That is the true role of the Master. Also, most imperative is to make the child move towards the Light and eventually become the Light. But unfortunately most people think otherwise. They feel it is the duty of the Master to change, manipulate their condition and situation and karma. Thus, when they go through a harsh period, they feel their Master has let them down.

'A Master can never let His or Her child down, but the laws of karma have to be obeyed and respected. If laws of karma, cause and effect, are not respected and upheld, then where is justice and law and order in the cosmos? The Master of course can postpone the inevitable and also can break the weight of the karmic baggage into smaller parts, but eventually the weight of the karmic baggage has to be carried. We are here to help each of you to finish off as fast as possible the karmic experiences, so that eventually you are free to move ahead and experience Oneness and Radiance, be filled with Oneness and Radiance and eventually become Oneness and Radiance. The more we allow procrastination of this, the more we are failing our children. Remember the only aim of life, for every living organism, is to merge and realize one's true origins and become One with the Fakir. This is and should be the only true priority of every individual. All other priorities are clouded with maya and illusion and wants and desires and duality. The Higher Self works towards this sole priority and the lower self tries everything possible to work against it. The Master stands between the higher and lower self, slowly helping the child to not only move towards the Higher Self, but to rest and operate from the Higher Self, not for a little while, but perpetually, and it is eventually this Higher Self which will make you realize your true Oneness.

'Thus every Master in reality is one who can see into the past, present and future. The miracles that take place are dependent on whether the Master feels that this is the appropriate time for the individual to face the experience or that the experience can be postponed till the child is more centred. If the Master feels the child will not be able to go through the karmic experience, and in fact going through the experience might break the child and slow down the process of spiritual growth and evolution or push the child to operate from the depths of the lower self, then the Master will use His or Her Grace to postpone the experience and this will appear to be a miracle.

'Say somebody for sure is going to get bankrupt but the Master realizes that this experience of bankruptcy will make the individual a bitter, mean, petty human being, which will make the individual create more karma, which would further add to the misery of the child for many future births. So the Master will save the child from the fire and it will appear to be a miracle. But, say, the Master feels that the experience is better to be faced and done with at that very moment, then the Master will not change the karmic timing and will let the child go through the experience. Remember, the experience will have to be undergone. There's no two ways about this.

'So RadhaKrishni had to go through the experience. In fact we made her go through it in such a horrific manner that it helped burn away all her pending karma caused by a very sharp, hurtful tongue and other past karmic baggage. We saved the child from falling into the fire as, first and foremost, the child was to be saved and also even if karma necessitated falling into the firepit, the mother would have got bitter, angry and depressed, and she would have created further karma which would have taken her lifetimes back in the journey of evolution. That is why Masters see into the past, present and future and decide what is best for the child. What we do is to give the child strength, wisdom, protection, calmness to go through his or her lot with positive acceptance and surrender but most often many do not want this grace from us. So do you understand the most important thing where the Master is concerned? He or She is only interested in your good and well-being and merger and is not trying to win a popularity contest.

'All the Master needs is love. Selfless love and complete surrender. This is all the Master truly seeks. When He or She gets this, the Master becomes a servant and slave of the disciple and for God's sake do not keep staring at me with your mouth agape, it is a ridiculously hilarious sight.'

> When an individual forgives or blesses somebody with
> a true heart, the dirt of past experiences, clinging to the
> aura, gets cleansed and the aura does not carry the past
> hurt and angst and the need for justice.

'Baba, I do not get this concept of charity.'

'Rabda, you are too kind to yourself. Why just the concept of charity? There is very little you understand of any concept.' Saying this Baba chuckled like a little boy and Rabda grimaced and then both the men began to laugh.

'*Ask and you shall receive, seek and you will find, knock and it will open to you*, Rabda, basically mean the same thing and all these phrases, are they not mentioned in the Bible?'

'I guess so, but I do not understand them.'

'Basically what do these phrases or assurance mean? One and the same thing—that Allah, God, Deva, Devi, the One, is most generous and merciful. Okay, let us start with the phrase "Ask and you shall receive". What does this mean? "Ask and you shall receive" seems a paradox, and most humans keep asking and most often they do not receive anything. "Seek and you fill find" and "Knock and it will open to you" mean the same. If you truly ask you shall receive what you are asking for. Well there are two pillars

71

to this phrase, which not many realize are the foundation of spirituality.'

'Oh boy, here we go again.'

'Shut up, boy, and listen with sheer wonder.'

'Yup, as though I have a blasted choice.'

'So, my dear brainless child who keeps trying to kill himself, the first component of this phrase is *ask. This simple word, ask, seems such a humble, silent, meek word, but no, it contains all the goodness of heaven and all the entrapments of hell and beyond.* Providence is all-benevolent. It wants to give you everything that can ascend you to the depth and merger with the One. It wants to give you everything that can help you move beyond the entrapments of illusion and make you soar to the seventh dimension of liberation. So, the most kind and benevolent and all-merciful and all-just Fakir wants you to ask for the springboard that can make you ascend to the very level of the One. We all come from Him and eventually our place is to merge with Him. So *ask* and plead and beg and yearn and cry each moment of your existence for help, love, blessings, grace to move beyond duality and into Oneness, as God is all-merciful and most generous. Thus, *ask* and S(H)e will give you what you want. There are no two doubts about this. *Ask* for the right things, bachcha, as when you ask for the right things, automatically you are making your priority clear to the cosmos. You *ask*, *seek*, *knock*, for help, grace, protection, calmness, strength, courage, joy, love; it means you need all these gifts to be centred to go through your lot with complete positive surrender and acceptance, thus making the One happy and proud of you. By *seeking* centredness to go through your lot calmly and wisely, you are sending a very clear message to the cosmos: that your priority is to serve and make the One happy and proud of your very breath and essence and conduct and very being. If one *knocks* at the doors of heaven for purity, calmness, wisdom, strength, to not only go through one's lot gracefully but to help others to go through their lot gracefully, the Lord opens the doors of heaven to you. This only means you are *asking* for something with the firm and clear intent that you want to walk the path, ascend beyond the laws of cause and effect and that your sole priority is to serve the Master and the One and thus move closer and closer to the Source and eventually merge with the Source, or serve the One; however S(H)e wants you to serve all of creation.

'So *ask*, *knock*, *seek* mean the same thing and are very powerful words, in fact the most powerful words.

'Extremely powerful, but it works both ways. *Ask* can become a ruthlessly self-destructive word too. If you *ask* for the wrong things, if you *ask* for things that take you away from the One; if you *seek* things that are going to further entrench you into the cesspool of karmic suffocation; if you *knock* on the door for something that causes somebody else pain and grief or destruction; if you *ask* for power and wealth for the wrong reasons, it is going to bind your legs, gag your mouth, strap your arms for lifetimes, with karmic ramifications.

'Also if you *ask, seek, knock* for anything other than what brings you closer to the One, your intent sends a message to the cosmos, that your priority is not the One, but everything else. I know you are not sleeping, Rabda, so stop trying to get smart with Sai.'

'My God, I wonder why I made the mistake to *ask* about *ask* . . .'

'So, my dear spiritual worm, I hope you got the first part of the phrases "Ask and you shall receive", "Knock and it will open to you" and "Seek and you shall find".

'Now comes the latter part of the phrase. *Receive, open, find.* What you receive or find or will be open to you is simple—it is whatever you have asked, sought, or knocked on the door for. The cosmos is going to grant all you want, all you pray for, all you seek and every time you knock on the doors of heaven, sooner or later the doors will open. And if you have not asked, sought, or knocked on the doors for the right reason, for the true Oneness reason, for being blessed with grace and wisdom but for reasons that take you away from the One, then you and your asking, seeking, knocking on doors is going to entrench you into the sinking sands of maya and karma—illusion and the laws of cause and effect.

'And if you have asked for the right reasons, then you can be assured that in this lifetime or the next, sometime or the other, your asking, seeking, knocking is going to bear fruit. So these phrases seem simple and sometimes even too good to be true, but the fact is this is the foundation of spirituality. Be careful, the path of spirituality has many landmines. Only a true Master can take you through the field without your being blown into smithereens.'

'Okay, sir, but what about charity? There are so many fakes going about asking for help, seeking money, knocking on the door for all kinds of assistance. What does one do and how does one know who is true and not?'

'Good question, Mr Rabda.'

'Please answer this question without now quoting some other phrase from the Bible, Quran, Avesta, Vedas, oh all-wise-and-with-all-the-time-in-the-world Master of mine.'

Baba let out a volley of swear words as though upset, but His eyes twinkled.

'Okay, let me start by making it clear that there are three reasons for compassion through giving, called charity. *The only true reason for giving selflessly is because it is the most noble thing to do. It brings a smile on your Master's face; it makes the angels sing, the heavens pray for you and God proud of you.* I say this with all honesty. Nothing makes the One more happy and proud of a child who gives selflessly, without agenda, without a motive, just for the glory of giving. Nothing makes God bless you and the angels pray for you more than when you indulge in an act of charity. So the only reason you should help others in the form of money, food, clothes, education, medicine, shelter, time, kindness, a smile, a helping hand, by just being a shoulder to cry on or a sounding board for somebody to pour out their frustration and sorrow and in countless other forms is because it makes the One happy and proud of you and prayers are said for your well-being by angels, not only for you but your family and loved ones of this life, past lives and future lives. There is a congregation of angels who do nothing but pray for the well-being of selfless helpers and their loved ones. Imagine, forty thousand angels praying for you every time you indulge in selfless charity.

'Now knowing your intelligence quotient, known as IQ, I am certain you must wonder what selfless giving or charity means. It means to give because you can feel the angst and tribulation of those in need of assistance. It means to give as we all are One and are connected more intimately than what is obvious. It means to give because when a child goes to sleep hungry, shivering or without medicine or shelter, you feel you have let God down. It means to give without the fear or wrath of God and without the need for praise or even blessings from God, Master and angels . . . to just give as it is the right thing to do and to come from compassion and empathy than from pity and well-clothed conceit. It means to give and yet feel you have done nothing, contributed a drop in the ocean and actually silently apologize to the cosmos for not being able to do more. It means to make the one you are helping or giving feel as though he or she is doing you a favour by accepting your gift or largeness of heart, never the other way round.

'When you give like this, forty thousand angels gather and pray for your well-being and the well-being of your loved ones, past, present, future, for those in the physical plane, those in the spirit plane and those in between. The more selfless your love, the greater the happiness all around. So my sweet, demented child, I am sure you have understood all I have narrated. Selfless giving makes the heavens sit up and sing your praises and makes the angels pray for you and your loved ones.

'I have said it time and again and it is even recorded in my Book: *Know for certain that he who feeds the hungry, really serves me with food. Regard this as an axiomatic truth . . .*'

'Ehhhh. What does the word axiomatic mean?'

'It means, obvious and without saying . . .'

'Then why use such fancy words like axiomatic . . .'

'You professional moron, I spoke these words in Hindi and Marathi, and then they were translated in English . . .'

'Ooooooooo . . . a Guru with temper and anger management issues . . .'

'Allah, have mercy and give me strength to abstain from the highest pleasure of breaking this child's vacant head . . . anyway, so when I said whoever feeds the poor feeds me, and this is the obvious truth, it also means that whoever helps the poor, helps me; whoever clothes the poor, clothes me; whoever educates the poor, educates me; whoever takes care of the ailing, helps me recover good health faster . . .'

'You know which phrase I loved of Yours? I think I fell in love with You once and for all, after reading a particular quote You had mentioned.'

Caiz went silent. Baba looked at him. After a while Baba stomped His feet.

'Which bloody quote, will you mention it or not?' he yelled.

'Okay, okay, telling you. I thought You could read my mind, so decided why bother repeating everything, which you already know. So the quote goes something like this . . .

'. . . Sitting in the masjid, I shall never ever speak the untruth . . . take pity on me . . . first give food to the hungry and then feed yourself. Note this well.'

'Yes, this quote and how You love showing off.'

Baba grinned. From ear to ear.

'Yes, I mean this, bachcha. If you take care of the poor, you are taking care of me, in more ways than you will ever know. So this is the first reason to help and give. This the first and the last reason to help and give but apart from having the angels pray for you and making your Master and God happy and proud of you, the other two benefits of giving selflessly are interesting too.'

'I guess till You do not divulge the other two benefits, this topic will go on and on. So go ahead, where am I going, first stuck in this strange cave with a Master who has anger management issues and then stuck in a dream where a Master keeps speaking and has funny golden stuff entering and leaving Him. Go ahead, Lord and Master, you have a captive, not captivated listener—a listener who is a captive.'

'Bloody idiot, keeps talking himself and then says the Sai talks,' Baba muttered under His breath. 'Okay, the first important thing that charity or selfless giving does is to work on your karma. Remember I had said that karma one has to go through? Well, selfless giving—remember selfless giving, not giving with an agenda, not giving to work out your karma, not giving to make the angels sing, but just selfless giving—helps to work out your karma.

'Very often karma is nothing but action, thought, word or intent, created by ignorance and selfishness. It is very often accumulated hurt, pain, humiliation and anger collected over lifetimes, now directed towards the concerned individual, so he experiences the very same feelings and situations, as he has, knowingly or unknowingly, caused pain to innumerable people through the journey of life. So, if somebody has hurt you, your heart has hurt and from the depth of your soul, pain has ensued and with that the need for justice. You can rest assured that whoever has hurt you, deceived you or done you wrong will have to experience the very same, and with compound interest, either in that particular lifetime or beyond. But let us say, for whatever reason, in that particular lifetime or in the next or whenever, you yourself bless that person, pray for his well-being, forgive him . . . and when you bless and pray for an individual on a higher level it means you have forgiven that person . . . then there is no hurt, no anger, no need for retribution in the person's aura, any more, and thus you have been absolved or released of the karmic give and take and karmic entrapment.

'Why this happens is because selflessly you gave, without any agenda, and who knows you gave that very individual you had caused pain to in some lifetime or you helped the descendent of the individual you have wronged, and now because of your selfless deed, the individual you have wronged has knowingly or unknowingly let go of the grudge and hate and pain caused lifetimes ago, and instead prayed for your well-being. So imagine, you just never know by a small act of kindness what a huge favour you have in reality done to yourself and your loved ones. The karma, all cause and effect, all hurt and angst, all experiences and their impact are in the aura of each individual. We have the physical body. Then we have the astral body. Then the causal body. Each religion will give these bodies various names. The physical contains all to do with the physical. The astral, all to do with the emotional. Causal, all to do with the mental and, mainly, as the word suggests, causal, cause and effect. When an individual forgives or blesses somebody with a true heart, the dirt of past experiences, clinging to the aura, gets cleansed and the aura does not carry the past hurt and angst and the need for justice. Once that happens, both the people, who may have lena-dena, or give and take with each other, are freed from that experience, thus one is freed from some unpleasant experience, due to a generous act of selflessness.

'Let us say, you have done something selflessly, but it has not touched the person who wants, consciously or karmically, to create another hole in your anatomy. Then too, the blessings of those you have helped sort of create a cushion, a wall of protection, so that when karma strikes, the intensity of the blow is reduced, as there are people praying for your well-being and safety. Prayers that have come from a heart filled with gratitude and love play the role of a serene oasis, when walking through the desert and hot sands of the laws of give and take, to take rest and be comforted. You are still in the karmic desert but because of all those you have helped, the desert is dotted with small oases, where you can take a bit of rest, drink cool water, sit under the shade and be comforted. The desert still is very much there and all its influences very much prevalent but the small oases can mean a matter of life and death, so as to speak.

'Also, the blessings and prayers of all those one has helped, along with the blessings and prayers of the angels, create a beautiful pathway when one has left the physical body. A lot of help is given in the spirit plane and then, of course, the most important thing, your future lives, either in the physical dimension or one of the spirit dimensions is taken care of in a profoundly substantial manner. Prayers and blessings which come from a true heart that has been helped form a kavach, a fortress around the individual and it goes a long, long, long way. Am tired of speaking and not knowing if anything is going through that funnily shaped head of yours. Anyway, the other reason for selflessly giving is very materialistic but then it exists so I'll tell you. Now listen with rapture and spellbound awe . . .'

'Oh, sweet Jesus on a bicycle.'

'I will pretend I cannot hear you. The second thing selfless giving does is to make sure you receive in abundance. If you give to the poor, even for karmic redemption, I will return to you tenfold and if you help those in need to make your Master happy and proud of you, I will give back to you a hundredfold and if you help those in need, selflessly, without thought of karma or Master, but just because you must, and that it is the right thing to do, the Oneness thing to do, then I shall give you back a forty thousandfold. This is the truth I speak. Let no being doubt this, for if the person doubts this truth, s(h)e doubts me and all that I stand for. Have not I said that the donor gives, that is, sows his seeds, only to reap a rich harvest in the future . . . wealth should be a means to work out dharma (responsibilities of brotherhood, as well as karmic and social responsibilities). If it has not been given before, you will not get it now. So, the best way to receive is to give. If you want to receive, give and even if you give to receive, it is still fine, as long as you are helping my children in need. Yes, what you shall receive when you give out of selflessness, with no karma or give and take in your mind, is something so abundant, that you will not be able to comprehend the gifts of bounty the cosmos shall shower you with.

'So imagine, if just a simple act of giving makes the One and all the Masters and the angels so happy, then there must be something very profound, something very spiritual, something very pure in the act of giving, that you have the heavens applauding and showering blessings and prayers on you. Then it works on your karma and either settles accounts or shields you with a protective blanket so that you are able to face your karmic blueprint in a calmer manner or dots your walk through the desert with small oases. And then the last: you are given either a minimum of ten times more or forty thousand times more, depending on the intention of why you've given and helped. Such a simple thing as giving means so much to the world beyond, bachcha. There must be something truly magical about this.'

'I have read that You used to ask people for a lot of money when they came to meet you in Shirdi. Sometimes You used to empty their pockets. You would even tell them to go and borrow money or beg to give You what You wanted?'

'Yes.'

'Why?'

'Let me explain to you one thing. Most of what is known about me is what happened ten years before I left my physical shell. Till ten years after my passing away, Shirdi was a small village and once in a while few people from nearby villages and towns and cities would visit. But those who came over came out of love for me or out of regard for my spirituality. Simple people came to me, Rabda. Very simple people, poor people, those who went through life just keeping their heads above water, keeping their bodies and souls together, trying their best to live a life with dignity and respect. They did not seek much from me but blessings, some guidance, some healing, and simple predictions. I was for most people a Muslim Sufi or a madman.

You see, my being in Shirdi had four phases. The first

phase was when I first arrived in this shell for a little while. Then I went away and came back to Shirdi nearly four years later in 1858. Then for nearly thirty years I was barely known anywhere, but amongst those who lived in Shirdi and surrounding areas and Sufis and yogis who came to meet me and be guided through me—they would quietly go away after spending a little while with me. So for thirty years I lived a life doing a lot of work in the spirit plane but in the physical plane I was sort of considered a mad Muslim fakir or just a madman.

'Then in the year 1886, I decided to leave the body, but my leaving the body is in the hands of the Fakir. My body was exhausted as I was taking on the misery and negativity of my loved ones who lived in Shirdi and beyond. I was doing a lot in the spirit world, helping my disciples, many of whom had not even heard of me. I was always tired of the body and wanted to move towards my Fakir. I knew it would require three days for me to make the final decision of staying in the spirit plane or returning into the body. But three days later I came into the body and people started coming from all over, but still the people came in a trickle. I would have enough time to myself and with my people. Then Das Ganu went all over the country and began to sing my songs and praise and thus from 1908, ten years before I left my body, my children from all over began to come. Sometimes on a single day there could be a few thousand and on Urus seventy thousand people. Each Master eventually wants to give time and attention to the real children, the real disciples, the real lovers, the real aspirants who want to walk the path. Most people come to a Master for material wealth and there is nothing wrong in that but even their coming is like a business deal: ask, take and fuck off. They do not care for God, the Master, giving the poor, nothing. It is all about I, *me*, *myself*. That is why sometimes a Master might either act mad or might do something which may offend society at large, or try to look like a power-hungry money-hungry, individual, as He or She wants the true lovers to come to the Master and the Source of Oneness. The true lovers know who the Master truly is. They are not fooled by the Master's idiosyncrasies. They love the Master irrespective of what the world says or feels or how the Master behaves.'

'Baba, I asked You a simple question and You as usual have woven the Bible around it. Just please in a few lines tell me why You used to often empty the pockets of those who came to be blessed by You? And Your time starts now—in two minutes tell me the answer, O Master with all the time in the world.'

'Shaitan, I am telling you. Listen quietly or I will break your fucking head.' Baba then kept abusing and muttering under His breath and then He smiled and all of creation smiled with Him.

'There are three reasons for asking for money . . .'

'Oh damn, damn, damn . . . always three reasons for everything, including farting I guess . . .'

'Oh yes, even for that, I can elaborate . . .'

'No, no, mai-baap, please carry on . . .'

'You look best in a coma, Rabda . . . anyway, the first reason is simple. The person owes something to the One. He or she or the family has pledged some money or some puja or some pilgrimage or the first salary to God, Goddess,

Master and have forgotten their pledge and if you have pledged something to Them, then it is my duty to claim what is mine. Also by claiming what is mine, I am protecting the family from the ramifications of a promise not kept with the One and the Oneness Family. When in need you promise Them something and then your work is done and you forget about the promise or keep postponing their rightful claim, then the cosmos sort of starts grinding its loins and tightening its balls, to show you your place. This is the law. *As you sow, you shall reap. What you promise, you shall keep.*'

Rabda groaned.

'Now you have begun to rhyme your sentences.'

'Yes, as obviously you cannot either rhyme or even kill yourself without giving the spiritual world above an excruciating migraine that starts from the lower part of the anatomy. So, the first reason I asked was because I knew what was owed and I wanted what was promised. Remember, I would keep nothing for myself. When I slept at night, I kept just some loose change, to buy my tobacco and oil for the lamps. Remember, only a Master knows what is truly owed by others to Him. So I could ask those who came and would keep asking till I got what was owed by them to the Oneness Family. I was actually saving the family too from letting the interest mount up to a level where sometimes the family would be wiped out of all their earnings.'

'But why does God or the Oneness Family care about repayment? They do not care about money or material things so why make such a fuss over money due to Them?'

'You idiot, it is not about money or material things. It

is about a promise. One shall not take the Lord's name in vain. So say all the ancient books. When you take the Lord's name in vain, the ramifications you shall face. That too is said in every ancient book. This is the way things are, Rabda. God is all-merciful but then God is all-just too. And justice demands that if you have made a pledge then you keep your promise to meet that pledge. Be it to God, Goddess, Master, human being, animal or to your own self. That is the law, Rabda. The law does not discriminate between the Oneness Family and an animal or anything. The law is the law. Final.

'So if somebody who had pledged something to the Oneness Family came, I made sure I took it out of that person. Before I slept, I, on that person's name or his or her family's name, would distribute that amount amongst the Sufis, yogis, householders and those in need. I have never needed money. I have told you, a Sufi or a man of God chooses poverty, voluntary poverty, as I have often said that poverty is the highest of the riches and superior to the Lord's position. God is the brother of the poor and a fakir is the real emperor. A fakir does not perish but an empire is soon lost. So for me, money does not matter.

'Then the second reason is that I want to test the disciples as to why they came to meet me.'

'Baba, You used to ask for much more than what they carried for the pilgrimage. If they had fifty bucks, You would ask for hundred and fifty and tell them to go beg, borrow and steal to give it to You. I mean, that was rather below the belt . . .'

'If only I had thrashed you below the belt each lifetime

you committed suicide because you wanted to be with me, I would have been a less angry man . . .'

'Ya, ya, ya but why ask so much from those poor bastards who came to meet You . . .'

'Because one needs to learn a few lessons before it is too late. First it is important to go beyond attachment towards money and wealth. Yes, if you have it, great, but if you have it and are obsessed with it then the wealth becomes your sinking sand, which is not good. Even poverty, if it makes you sad, mean, bitter, jealous, is a horrible thing. Thus voluntary poverty and detached affluence are both one and the same thing. If you are poor and bitter about it or you are rich and obsessed about it, it means the same. But a rich man who is detached about his wealth is on the same page as a poor man who has accepted his lot with calm and positive acceptance. It is all about how one embraces each situation.

'So, son, I would ask or empty pockets because either I wanted the individual to shed his attachment to money or decide whether I am more important or the money he or she carries. If I am important, if the Master is important, then there would be no shame or ego in even going forth and begging or asking for help to secure the money that is asked by me. So, first and foremost, the love and surrender you have for your Master will decide your reaction and behaviour towards the Master's request about something. Of course, the Master has to be truly pure. That comes from not keeping anything for Himself or Herself. Or not being attached to anything that is asked for.

'The third reason is that I wanted to avoid those who did

not come out of love but came for selfish interests only. Yes, everybody has some hidden interest in their devotion too. That is fine. But some are not interested in God or anything that is on the path. They are only interested, crab-like, in their small world of money, position, power, ego, the worldly shit of glitter. So I wanted to shoo those people away till they realized the importance of detachment and the position of a Master.

'Now your question as to how to know who is truly deserving and who is not is up to your discretion and judgement. If you feel somebody is in true need, give without worrying about whether the person's motives are pure or not. If the person is trying to cheat you, the cosmos will deal with the person in the way the cosmos knows best. It will extract a hundred- or thousandfold from that person in some way or the other. The cosmos is ruthless when it has to be. So do not worry about this.

'I have mentioned it time and again that if someone begs (or asks for help) for anything and if that is in your power and if you can grant the request, give it. Do not say no. But if you have nothing to give the person (or do not want to give for whatever the reason), give a polite negative reply but do not mock or ridicule the person nor get angry with him and make sure you do not shoo him away. And this applies to man, woman, child, animal, bird or whosoever, it does not matter. You give if you can and if you cannot or do not want to then do so with respect. Join your hands and request the person to forgive you or understand that you cannot meet that person's request or demand. And if you give help, do not seek anything in return, not even gratitude. As that will create a karmic cycle with you and the individual.'

'Meaning?'

'Let us say a beggar comes and wants money from you. If you do not want to help out, say a polite no. If you do help out, give the money because you want to truly help the person and relieve him of his plight. Say, you feel he is hungry or thirsty, give him money for food or water or whatever, because you do not want another being to go without food or water or whatever it is the person seeks money for. Do it because you want to help the person out for the sake of Oneness and compassion. Then there is no give and take between you and the person. But if you give the person hoping for blessings, hoping for gratitude, hoping that your Master sees the act and is thrilled about your kindness, then you begin the play of give and take. The karmic bond between you and the person begins. Then you will somehow or the other have to come to receive that money from the same individual, in this lifetime or the next. Thus, when you help, help without any agenda. Yes, you will be blessed with much more, but then the karmic ranubhandha or bond with the individual and you has begun. And remember, there is a difference between charity and compassion. In charity you give. In compassion you share. When you give, you have to receive the same too from the same individual. When you share, it spreads a bond of giving, which goes on for lifetimes, with or without you.

'From your face, which is a painting in complete dumbfounded blankness, it is obvious you have not understood the last part of what I said to you. What I mean is this. When you give out of compassion, it is selfless giving.

You want nothing in return. Now the one you have helped is in debt, no longer with you but with the cosmos. Now that person will have to return the kindness to somebody else. The chain continues. If the person were to give out of compassion, then the third person again has to give what is to be given to another person outside the chain of give and take. So one's small act of compassion has then formed a chain of giving. But in charity, if there is any self involved in the process of giving then what you give, you shall receive, in this lifetime or the next or after that. Thus, that giving and taking is limited to two individuals.

'But remember one thing. Do not be an idiot while helping somebody. There are many in need. Help those truly in need or at least try your best to help those truly in need. You might still be fooled; then leave it to Allah to sort things out. And yes, not many remember what I have said about compassion and humility. Always be humble and compassionate but humility should not be towards all . . . Severity is necessary in dealing with the wicked. Those who are wicked, deal with them in the way they deserve—not out of anger, or hate or revenge but, as Lord Krishna says, the idea of do not do evil and do not bear evil. When you do evil it is wrong, but when you turn a blind eye to evil or quietly bear the evil deed, you are encouraging the evil person to go further into the bowels of hell. The person gets more power to do further evil. By standing up to evil and evildoers, you are doing two things. Protecting the innocent and making sure that evil does not get perpetuated and also you are helping the evil person not go further into the abyss of hell. Do you understand, you mystified cow?'

'One simple question you ask and You just do not stop. Hmmmmm . . . Stupefied at your vocal stamina.'

Baba began preparing a chillum, silently muttering under His breath. Then He looked up at Rabda with the eyes of the Goddess of Maternal Love and Rabda began to cry. He walked towards Baba and put his head at His feet and began to sob, while the Old Man caressed his head and said, 'Allah bhala karega, do not cry . . . oyyye Rabda, fikar not, your Baba is with you and His children, for now and beyond the beyond.'

'Baba, I want to see the time You went into Your first samadhi for three days. Also, tell me, You used to ask for specific amounts as dakshina or money from certain devotees. Any particular reason?'

'Bachcha, all my life I begged for my food from five homes. All my life. So there is always a reason for me to ask anything from anybody. I did not need anything but I would go each day, sometimes fifteen times a day, to beg for my food, which I shared with one and all; I barely ate, have no taste on my tongue, thus if I asked for something, there was and is always a reason.'

'Baba, can you explain all this to me in a concise manner. I know You have all of eternity but You must know I am on borrowed time.'

'You are the worst comedian ever, Rabda . . .'

'I take after my grumpy Guru . . .'

Baba muttered various imaginative abuses and then smiled.

'I ask from no one, Rabda. It is the One, the Fakir, Allah, who directs me to ask from certain individuals and makes sure I refuse from other individuals. I need no money, bachcha. What will a poor fakir do with money anyway? I have no responsibilities but that of keeping oil in the lamps, a few logs of wood for Dhuni Mai and for my tobacco. Thus, often I was not asking for money, bachcha, but asking for other things, so so so much more important than all the money put together in all of creation. Also it was only when devotees began to first come by the hundreds and then by the thousands that I began to ask for money, otherwise I never asked for money from anybody. Thus, it was virtually in the last fourteen years of my life that I began to ask for money to ascertain various things apart from the intensity of love, faith and devotion. Each time I asked for a specific amount there was a divine reason to it.'

Caiz was more than aware that where Baba was concerned everything began and ended with love. If there was love, the Master was bonded to the individual. If there was business, then the Master was a ruthless businessman and the books of accounts had to be perfectly balanced—no ifs and buts.

Even when Baba Sai asked for money or dakshina, He was not interested in the money. What would Baba do with money? He had embraced poverty like a lover does his beloved. By the time Baba was preparing for His samadhi, He cumulatively every month received more money than the British governor of India but every night before He slept, He distributed all that money to the poor, the Sufis, the sages, to some of His devotees and for repairing temples in and around Shirdi and sponsoring pilgrimages in the country and the hajj. So why would Baba often empty the pockets of those who came to meet Him? Why would He sometimes keep asking for money from the same person, refusing money from those who stood by, but empty the pocket of that individual and still ask for more?

'For instance, when I asked for two paise or two rupees, I was in reality asking for faith and patience. The same way the Holy Ash from Dhuni Mai was to teach one and all that eventually the body will become dust but the spirit and the soul would always be eternal. And me asking for money was also to teach one and all about detachment from what ails all of mankind, the need to amass wealth for personal consumption, rather than to share it with those in true need.

'When I asked for one paisa or rupee I was asking for Oneness and to banish discrimination in the name of God and religion. When I asked for three paise or rupees, I wanted the belief in the Trinity and also I wanted complete devotion and surrender of body, mind and soul, and everything to do with the physical, emotional and mental. I wanted surrender of the mind, the intellect and knowledge to be laid at the feet of God, Goddess and Master.

'When I asked for four paise or rupees, I wanted the child to give me in addition to the mind and intellect also their various planes of consciousness and their ego and pride. Or I wanted the child to focus on the four main reasons or purpose or principles of life. The first is dharma, that is, respecting one's station, duties and responsibilities in life, and accepting one's station in life without resentment, without envy and without greed. Then comes karma, which means respecting the laws of cause and effect and accepting the ramification of one's actions and decisions and the use of free will, either in past lives or the present. Then comes the need for shunya, which means the need to be free from the ramifications of cause and effect and thus conducting oneself in a manner that releases oneself from the charkhi or wheel or the sinking sand of cause and effect. And the last is moksha, which means to be liberated from all ignorance and prejudices and dogmas and go beyond everything and to merge with the One.

'When I demanded five paise or five rupees, I wanted the child to lay at my feet all the five senses: taste, touch, smell, sight and hearing. If you can get your breath under control, all these five senses come under control. But then who wants to waste time breathing in and out when there are so many outwardly sensual gratifications taking place?

'I asked for six paise or six rupees when I wanted as dakshina the six enemies of all beings, the inner lower energies that come in a pack of six, uncontrolled desires and attachments, greed, anger, jealousy, hate and ego. The six enemies who have managed to outwit and overcome sages, Sufis, saints, priests and monks as well as warriors, leaders, captains of industries, artists, scientists, doctors, social workers, and of course the salt of the earth, the so-called common man.

'When I asked for seven paise or seven rupees, I wanted the individual to let go of all thoughts of the seven dimensions and the astral and causal worlds, of heaven and hell, of spirits and astral travel, and focus on the now, the present, to give life his or her best and leave the rest to one's Master and one's destiny and lot.

'When I sought eight paise or rupees, ten paise or rupees or eighteen paise or rupees, I wanted the person to surrender to me all paranormal powers he or she had acquired through means that were not right or were questionable. These powers are called sidhis. There can be eight sidhis, or ten sidhis or, all put together, eighteen such sidhis. If the individual is not pulsating with Oneness and to serve God, Goddess and Master only, but to serve himself or herself and fan his or her ego, the powers are being used or were going to be used not to spread Light and compassion but to avail oneself of power and heighten one's greed and thus hasten one's descent into the bowels of hell, all the while hurting and cheating innocent people and breaking their trust in God, Goddess and Master and the purity and sanctity of the path, then I want the surrender of all those sidhis and intentions. Remember it is better to face agony and misfortune than to court these lower powers and sidhis, as such powers are like a prostitute who, though she can earn through hard work, uses her body to entice and earn quick money. Avoid such powers, as that is a sure way to the worst possible hell ever created by God in His benevolent wisdom.

'When I sought nine rupees or nine paise, bachcha, I wanted the child to lay down the hold of astrology and the nine planets and the influence, positive and negative, the nine planets exerted consciously or subconsciously in the child's life. The planets shall do their work based on one's karma, but always remember, prayers, meditation, compassion, charity, the Master and, most important, the grace of God and Goddess can perform miracles and that nothing is impossible for Allah. Thus, respect the planets but to be obsessed or fearful of Them does not speak much for the child's faith in his or her own individual capacity and potential and also does not take into account the power of the beyond, which is far beyond the influence of planets and all lines on one's palms and in the cards.

'So you defrosted ape, always remember that if your Baba asked for dakshina it was not for my well-being but for the spiritual well-being of the individual asked. I used to ask for fifteen and fifty and hundred and sixteen and a half, and each time it depended on the individual. Sometimes me asking for fifty-three rupees would mean I wanted the individual to read the Guru Charitra which comprised of fifty-three chapters. I knew what I was being asked to ask the devotee by the Fakir and My Beloved. *I need nothing but love. I need nothing but unquestionable surrender and faith. Beyond that what can anybody give me that matters to me?* From you though I will have to ask for a few thousand rupees, one or two rupees will not do for you, you terribly out-of-tune musician.'

'Oh ya, humour it is. Ha ha ha.'

'Come, we go back to Shirdi, you constipated worm.'

And in a second they were back in Shirdi. The first time people, especially Hindus, began to sit up and take notice of Baba Sai—till now known by just a few outside Shirdi and the nearby villages and towns as a madman or a powerful though extremely eccentric Sufi—was in the year 1878, when the Guru of all Gurus, the powerful, no-nonsense, exceedingly to-the-point, to many orthodox but to all the most tender, benevolent, powerful Guru, Swami Samarth of Akalkot, just before He took samadhi, told one and all, that He was not leaving His children and devotees. If they wanted to meet Him, all they had to do was to go to Shirdi, meet Him in the fakir Sai, Sai Baba of Shirdi.

Swami Akalkot was loved and worshipped by countless devotees. His telling His close disciples that Sai Baba and He were one indicated two things clearly. First and foremost, Masters are beyond religion and duality. Second, Swami Akalkot was and is considered an avatar or reincarnation of Lord Dattatreya; Him saying He and Baba Sai are One, it meant Sai too was One with Lord Dattatreya and those who stayed away from Baba because of His unorthodox behaviour or Sufi appearance were made to understand that even if Swami Akalkot had left His body, He resided in Sai Baba of Shirdi. Slowly, thus, people started coming to Shirdi to see and meet and pay obeisance to the Man who the great and powerful Swami Akalkot had directed towards.

But all the while Baba continued to live in His humble manner and it made no difference to Him whether He was considered a God or a mad fakir. His main people were Mahalsapati, Tatya and Shama, though a number of those who lived in Shirdi and nearby villages had begun to consider Baba their Guru.

It was the year 1886. On 14 August, Caiz saw Baba Sai exceedingly ill. Baba suffered from severe asthma which often made Him gasp for breath. His breathing would get so laboured that often those close to Him would begin to weep, unable to see Baba's suffering. Baba would smile and tell one and all not to worry, this is what the Fakir wanted Baba to go through, so be it.

Also Baba seemed to be tired and longing to merge with the One. He never said it openly but He looked tired. There was so much work taking place in the spirit dimension, with Baba helping scores of people go through their lives with dignity, the strange part being most of those were not even aware of Baba or His help and presence. But Caiz understood that Masters are not concerned about personal glory or fame or adulation. They work and help and heal and bless and take on the suffering of Their lot silently.

Caiz saw Rabda sitting close to Baba Sai. The young man was visibly upset seeing Baba's suffering. So many spirit helpers surrounded Baba, all in prayer, all aware of what was to come about.

Baba walked near a particular spot in Dwarka Mai with the help of Mahalsapati. It was a full-moon night. A beautiful day to do what He had to, sighed Baba Sai. He lay His head on Mahalsapati's lap. It was obvious Baba was going through excruciating discomfort but He smiled, as though reassuring Mahalsapati not to worry.

'Bhagat, listen, be careful,' Baba whispered, as He laboured to speak. 'Allah has decided that I leave this body . . . don't get worried . . . listen to Me. Allah has permitted me to leave this body as it needs to be cleansed and this cleansing cannot be done with me in the body. I will leave this body in some time. Everybody will think I have died. My body will show no signs of life, bachcha, but remember one thing, the way I see it, I will return to my body in three days. If I don't return to this battered body, then you see that plot of land, bury me there and put two flags, one near my head and the other on the left side of my body, to indicate that Sai's body rests in this spot.'

'Baba . . .'

'You will have to protect my body, Bhagat. My blessings are with you and remember whether I return or not, I am with you and all those who are mine. Allah Malik.'

Saying this, Baba exhaled the sigh of release and slumped deeper into the lap of the visibly weeping Mahalsapati. Thus on a full-moon night on 14 August, Baba left His mortal remains. In a short while, the news spread like wild fire. Tatya and Shama came running, weeping as though possessed but the moment Mahalsapati explained to them what Baba had revealed, they stopped weeping and embraced each other. They knew their Old Man. For Baba everything and anything was not only possible but mundane. Miracles were made to look like daily routine where Baba was concerned so the two men formed a protective ring round Baba and Mahalsapati.

There were many who thought Baba was just a madman or, worse, a fake. Those who wanted to get rid of Baba began to insist that Baba be buried at the earliest. First, doctors from the villages came and checked Baba and declared Him dead. Then the British administrators, hearing about the strange happenings in Shirdi—a fakir who was apparently dead but clearly with all intentions of returning to His body—sent their English medical officer.

The young man came over on the third day of Baba leaving His body. Baba lay with His head on Mahalsapati, who had not got up once. Shama who was a huge and robust man stood with a sturdy bamboo stick in his hand, daring anybody to come close to his Baba. Tatya, known in the village, used all his influence to galvanize support from the villagers to safeguard Baba's body. Thus, those who loved Baba formed a protective human shield around Baba and Dwarka Mai.

So the English doctor came over, examined Baba, declared

Him dead but also made it clear that Baba exhibited no sign of having been dead for three days as the body was still relaxed and rigor mortis, or the stiffening of the body, surprisingly had not set in. He was confused but very politely suggested that Baba was dead and with the scare of cholera and typhoid, it would be best to bury Baba. But one look from Shama, who understood English perfectly and also had the body of a pit bull terrier, and the medical officer sighed and left.

In the early hours of the fourth day's morning, before dawn, Baba's breathing commenced, His stomach showed the movement of inhalation and exhalation and after a while, whispering 'Allah Malik', Baba opened His eyes and smiled. He stretched His body as though waking up from a long slumber and sat up. Mahalsapati began to weep and Shirdi erupted with screams of joy, and all those in their houses ran out to see the miracle.

A few days later Mahalsapati asked Baba why the three-day samadhi. Baba smiled.

'I was tired of living. My body was plagued with pain, agony and taking on the suffering of my lot and working out their karmas along with them. I was tired, Bhagat. I wanted to go back to Him. So I decided to end my life and go back to Allah. But obviously Allah had other plans. My friend and brother, Gadhadhar, who the world knows as Rama Krishna Paramahamsa, had also decided to leave His body; His work was not finished but He wanted to merge with Ma. Only one of us could remain and so I decided to come back and let my friend and brother continue His journey upwards.'

One day later the newspapers published the heartbreaking

news of Shri Rama Krishna Paramahamsa taking samadhi in Calcutta, on 16 August. The British doctor came back to find Baba smoking a chillum. The poor man nearly passed out. He turned towards his fellow officers and then looked at Baba and Baba smiled and the officer gasped in disbelief as he saw his Lord and Master, Jesus Christ, in Baba.

'Like my Christ, Baba was resurrected after three days. You do not know how fortunate you are to be living so close to Him.' Saying this, he bowed to Baba who nodded back, and then left.

Caiz looked at Baba sitting in Dwarka Mai, in front of the Holy Fire, chanting, while innumerable spirit bodies circled around Him, saying their individual prayers.

Back in the cave, Caiz sat silently in front of the Fire. He was so overwhelmed seeing everything and realizing everything about Baba that all he could do then was approach Baba, put his head down at Baba's feet and cry.

Far away the nurse again noticed tears gushing down the cheeks of her famous patient. He seemed to be glowing now. As though the coma was in reality doing wonders for his health in a strange way.

> When you share, it spreads a bond of giving, which
> goes on for lifetimes, with or without you.

After Baba's three-day samadhi, Mahalsapati first and then after a while Shama began to spend every night with Baba Sai at Dwarka Mai. Caiz had always been interested in experiencing those nights Baba and His two disciples, worshippers and friends spent making certain the others did not sleep. This was Baba's way of helping them be in constant remembrance of God. For Baba not sleeping much meant more time being in awareness of God's creation, being in gratitude of God's glory and being filled with God's energy and presence. *Even if a person would spend time just alone, on and off chanting His Name, drop by drop the ocean would fill.*

Baba all His life had slept in Dwarka Mai, but one day it began to pour. Caiz felt that the humble structure of the old masjid would collapse. Dwarka Mai was a very small structure unlike the one that now is in Shirdi. It was made of mud and the floor was covered with cow dung. The strong winds brought the rain into Dwarka Mai and Baba was only concerned about protecting the perpetual Fire that burnt. The water had begun to slowly collect in Dwarka Mai, and all those present within pleaded with

Baba to move to Chavadi, the rest house which was not more than twenty or thirty feet adjacent. There was a lane that separated Dwarka Mai and Chavadi. Down the lane was Baba's favourite Lord Hanuman temple, which was near a huge beautiful tree.

Baba began to abuse one and all. He was against any kind of change. He liked to have a routine. He liked things as they were. However old, dirty, dilapidated something was, Baba was happy with the familiarity of things. Thus, everybody was aware that to convince Baba to leave Dwarka Mai was going to be a herculean task. Eventually Narayan Teli could no longer stand seeing Baba all drenched and the thought of Baba spending a night there while it stormed outside was too much for the good man. So he approached Baba, apologized for what he was about to do and quickly picked Baba up and put Him on his shoulders and quickly ran to Chavadi.

Caiz began to laugh and Baba who stood by his side began to mutter but He chuckled too.

'The haramkhor just picked me up and ran like a shaitan!'

All the while Narayan Teli ran as though possessed, Baba abused loudly. All the beautiful words created in Persian, Arabic, Hindi and Marathi were used on Teli but Teli ran, disregarding all that Baba abused him with.

They entered Chavadi, Baba holding on to the man's shoulder, shouting and screaming at one and all, and the others for a moment stood with mouths agape, not believing what Teli had done. But once within the safe confines of Chavadi, Baba cooled down, patted Teli and then henceforth every alternate night Baba would sleep in Chavadi.

In Chavadi He slept in the right side of the room while Mahalsapati and other devotees would sleep in the other room.

Abdul had arrived in Shirdi a year after Baba's first samadhi but he was not given lodging or boarding by Baba. He had to fend for himself.

Every night in Dwarka Mai, Mahalsapati and Tatya would sit and chat through the night. Baba would be like a friend to both of them. He would tell them stories of distant places He had travelled to safeguard His devotees and in a few days news would trickle in to confirm what Baba had revealed to both of them.

In the night only Laxmi Ma, as Baba Sai fondly called her, was allowed to enter Dwarka Mai. She was beloved to Baba. She had served Baba for forty-five years and was one of the first to feed Baba and, when Baba Sai took samadhi, was the last to be with Him. She loved Him dearly and Laxmi Ma would be allowed access to Him any time and any place. In fact later when the crowds of devotees would grow, Baba still would give special place of honour and love to Laxmi Ma. He would call for kheer, sweet rice and milk, and take a few bites and, through her hands, make the kheer reach RadhaKrishna Mai, who loved kheer and would only eat what Baba sent to her as her prasad.

Caiz saw Rabda sit with Baba Sai while He spoke to Mahalsapati and Tatya through the night. In fact even after Baba took samadhi thirty-two years later, Mahalsapati would continue to sit all day in Dwarka Mai and every alternate night sleep in Dwarka Mai till he passed over four years later.

Baba, Mahalsapati and Tatya would sleep with their heads towards the east, west and north, their feet touching each other in the centre of the mosque, like spokes of a wheel. Baba would be in the middle with His head towards the west, which meant His head was facing the direction of the Holy Kaaba, assumed Caiz. Till midnight and beyond they would talk and then for a very short time before dawn Baba would allow them to sleep.

If Tatya began to snore, as he was the first to always fall asleep, Baba would get up and shake him or turn him from one side to the other or make him turn on his stomach and gently press his head to the ground or Tatya would be sandwiched between Baba and Mahalsapati, both hugging the man close or Baba even pressing Tatya's feet or kneading his back.

There were times Baba would press Tatya's feet or Mahalsapati's legs and when they objected Baba would say, 'For the world I am may be Guru or even God, but here, in Masjid Ayi (Dwarka Mai) we are friends all moving towards Him.'

But what made Caiz really buckle up with laughter was while Tatya slept, Baba would hide Tatya's belongings and when Tatya woke up Baba would go all out of His way to pretend to help Tatya find the belonging or Baba would gently, with Mahalsapati's help, lift Tatya up and place the poor chap outside Dwarka Mai and then the two would wait like children for Tatya to wake up in a state of shock, wondering how on earth he had managed to land up in the middle of the lane. And many times Baba and Mahalsapati would pretend to be sleeping, all the while chuckling while watching Tatya enter Dwarka Mai all confused, scratching his head in bewilderment.

But obviously, after a few times Tatya the genius realized what was going on and he, tall and strong, would pick Baba up on his shoulders and run through the length and breadth of Dwarka Mai, with Baba, unable to keep His laughter under check, abusing and telling him to either put Him down or not run like a horse in heat and slow down. Baba once wore Tatya's turban and mimicked Tatya so well that all the three men rolled on the floor with laughter.

They would smoke the chillum often and there were times when Tatya arrived really tired, and both Baba and Mahalsapati would press his body and feet, which really riled Tatya, as for him, Baba was his Guru and God. Once he had got so upset that for nights he refused to come and sleep in Dwarka Mai till somehow Baba persuaded him and then Tatya began to cry, saying not to add to his karma by pressing his feet, he a sinner, while Baba was his Trinity.

Caiz had tears in his eyes when one day he saw Baba and Mahalsapati sitting in Dwarka Mai, and they saw Nana Chandorkar, another intimate disciple performed by Baba. Nana was fortunate to have witnessed personally many miracles performed by Baba, even the one where the Holy Ash was delivered to his doorstep, with the horse carriage materializing in the middle of the night hundreds of miles away to take the carrier of the Holy Ash to Nana's doorstep. But when this incident took place Nana was still to come into Baba's fold.

'Bhagat, who is that chap standing there?'

'Baba, that is Nana.'

'Achha, that is Nana. Arrey Bhagat, this Nana wants to work on our Masjid Ayi and wants to virtually reconstruct our Masjid Ayi as he feels the masjid has become very old and he wants to make it pucca, strong, he said. What do you think, Bhagat, should we allow changes to be made to our masjid? Is something wrong with our masjid? What do you think, do you feel it requires any change? You know me, Bhagat, I am not much for change. Simplicity and familiarity and routine comforts me. It lets me focus on what should be truly permanent and the changes that are really needed for each individual, which are always internal.'

'Baba, let him do what he wants. He can't change the essence as that is You and our Holy Fire. The walls and floors do not make Dwarka Mai. You and Your Energy and presence and our Dhuni Mai makes the essence and, my Sai, we will be able to sit and sleep a little more comfortably.'

Baba lit a chillum. Muttered abuses galore. Chuckled. Smiled. Nodded, giving His permission.

Baba thus gave His consent, but what was more beautiful was the innocence Caiz witnessed in Sai, who was so often as innocent as a child.

One needs to be careful of desires as once you have your desires under your control, you shall move into the region of the heart.

For fourteen years, from 1898 to 1912, Mahalsapati, Tatya and Baba spent such beautiful nights. So much of love and so much of laughter and blessings, but once Tatya's father passed away, Baba insisted that Tatya take up the family responsibility and thus after fourteen years, till Baba took samadhi, Mahalsapati spent every night with Baba, either at Dwarka Mai or often even at Chavadi.

Many miracles took place after Baba's three-day samadhi, but noteworthy for Caiz was a particular incident which he had grown up hearing about from his maternal grandmother and mother.

This was Baba's unusual sleeping place in Dwarka Mai. Apart from being able to remove His intestines to be washed and also separate His limbs, the ultimate yoga practices known to Masters, Baba would sleep on a thin plank, suspended seven feet above the ground; Baba was five feet six inches tall. The plank was somehow attached to the beams of Dwarka Mai, by thin pieces of cloth. It was in the year 1898 that a gentleman by the name of Dengle had gifted Baba a wooden plank, which was about four and a half feet long and less than a foot wide. Now on the four corners of the plank Baba would place earthen oil lamps which burnt all night long.

And somehow Baba managed to not only get on this high plank but even sleep on it. Baba would then either sit in prayer or lie down. He never really slept but still if He did dose off, strict instructions were given to Mahalsapati (as till then Tatya had not begun to sleep in Dwarka Mai) that He should be awakened. He did not want to spend a moment away from God-awareness and chanting God's name.

When Baba realized that the curiosity of how He managed to get on the plank and sleep on it and how the plank suspended with the help of thin strips of cloth could bear, forget Baba's weight, the weight of the plank itself, got the better of the devotees and village folks, especially children, one day Baba after screaming abuses and running out to hit one and all, came back, broke the plank and offered the wood to the Holy Fire.

When He was asked why He did what He did, Baba said, 'Why should I sleep on the plank and my Mahalsa sleep on the floor? . . . It is better he should sleep on a higher place than me.'

This is when Caiz realized the love Baba has for all His disciples. Mahalsapati was not a devotee of Baba, he was Baba's disciple, as for Mahalsapati, life began and ended with Baba, and Baba's will was Baba's wish and command, no ifs and buts, no questions asked, no consequences debated or questioned. A disciple lives and breathes his or her Master whereas for a devotee, the Master is part of his or her life;

for a disciple the Master is Life, Death, Soul, Liberation and Merger.

So by Baba saying let Mahalsapati sleep higher than Him, Baba meant that He wanted His children to merge with the One, while He as the Master would guide each one to the Final Destination, but He would always remain one rung lower, in order to ferry each and every disciple to the One.

Caiz looked at Rabda who was always near Baba and for the first time envied Rabda, who was in reality himself. He realized one thing. He did not want liberation, happiness, joy, ecstasy and even Godhood. All he wanted was to always be near his Baba Sai: his God, Guru and a phenomenal grumpy Old Man.

They were back in Shirdi. Once again Abdul and Rabda, along with innumerable spirit bodies, sat with Baba. It was a cold afternoon. Outside, Caiz was shocked to see countless devotees milling around Dwarka Mai, while a number of devotees, including Shama, Mahalsapati, Tatya, Nana and other close and old followers of Baba made certain that Baba was given His afternoon two or more hours of rest or prayers and meditation. Obviously this particular incident must have taken place after 1910, as it was then when countless people who, inspired by the songs of Das Ganu—once-upon-a-time police constable and lyrist of lewd plays with a lot of sexual innuendo, called tamashas, who was now the foremost poet and musician to spread Baba's name and glory through all of Maharashtra and eventually all over the country—would flock to Shirdi. Shirdi looked different. There were two quarters to live in for devotees made by wealthy devotees of Baba, Sathe Wada and Dixit Wada. But through it all, Baba sat unperturbed and unchanged, still in His torn or stitched-in-innumerable-places kafni, His once-white bandana now light brown. The same atmosphere in Dwarka Mai. The same peace and warmth. Dhuni Mai burning peacefully. A curtain was drawn to accord Baba some privacy which was ample for Him. He sat smoking His chillum and speaking softly to Abdul.

'Baba, a lot of people see various avatars in you. They say you are Datta Guru and You are Lord Rama and You are Shiva. Who are You, Baba?'

'Abdul, I am Allah's slave. I will always be Allah's servant. I want to be nothing but what Allah wants me to be. Who am I? I come from the One. I serve the One. In the One I repose. With the One I shall one day merge. But till the One decides what the One decides, I, the breath of Allah, will continue doing what His Master and Beloved wants out of me.'

There was a sigh that Caiz and Rabda could hear. The sigh came from the innumerable spirit bodies that had gathered to hear Baba speak. The place was so charged that Energy that circulated within Dwarka Mai reached out and cleansed all those who had come to meet Baba Sai. Now Caiz realized the importance of pilgrimages and being in the presence of a Master. The Energy is so vibrant and so vast and all-pervasive that even when one cannot see or meet the Master or be in the sanctum sanctorum or in front of the God, Goddess, Fire, or whoever presides in the holy place, the Energy emitted does wonders and, best of all, the Energy works on all: sages, devotees, sinners, lay people, all. Like the rays of the sun which never discriminates, the Energy of the Master is for all; now how the Energy is received, whether doors are shut or curtains put up to ward off the rays of the sun, that depends on each individual.

'Remember, Abdul, not many will tell this, but there have been, are and will be thousands of avatars in the age of Kaliyuga.' Caiz saw Abdul write things down but in his own quick way so as to keep up with Baba. 'At this point and always, there are nearly twenty avatars all living at one time, often unknown or known to each other. Many avatars are not aware of Their Godhood. That way, Abdul, are we all not avatars? We come from Him. We belong to Him. We are filled with Him. So we are avatars but most have their Godhood under the wreckage and weight of karma. And so all are avatars in various degrees of self-realization or ignorance.

Then Caiz saw Abdul write quickly what Baba dictated. Jali (water) Avatar and then Thali (land) Avatar, then Brahmin (Yamana), then the Rajput (Rama), then Gavli (Krishna) and then Musalmans. In the subloka all the people were indifferent. There were four avatars in Kritayuga (Matsya, Kurna, Yaraha and Narasimha) and three avataras in the Treta (Yamana, Parasurama and Rama) and two avatars in Dwaparayuga (Krishna and Balarama). Thereafter two avatars, Shesha and Kalanki, are listed, who are referred to in Islam as Mehdi and Alehussalman. After Maccha, Kaccha, Yaraha, Narasimha, Parasurama, Krishna, they list Ibrahim, Kalanki, Alehussalman and Buddha. Thus, there is One God and there are thousands of avatars in the Kaliyuga. The methods of worship for everyone are different. The present Kaliyuga avatar is Sai Baba.

This is what Abdul wrote in Urdu.

'But Baba, the Sufis state that the world is looked after by the Masters.'

'Yes, but even here there are a lot of divisions and sub-divisions. You have first the Qutub or Qutb Aaqtab, who is the Supreme Head of all. Under Him are twelve qutubs, or qutbs. This has always been and will always be. If One of Them leaves the body, another immediately takes His place.

'Then under the qutub is one ghaus and then there are two imans. Then you have seven main abdals, who are in charge of the spiritual empire.'

Caiz understood this as the spiritual dimensions. Seven dimensions being looked after by seven Abdals.

'Thus each empire has one abdal, and under Them are three hundred and seventy-five abdals or powerful agents or helpers of God, whose main function is to help and assist those in true need of spiritual, material and all kinds of assistance. The abdals usually stay in jungles and in the mountains and of these some abdals are also called abrar.

'Under these abdals are four autads, who live in the four corners of the world and look after the peace in the world, or whatever peace there is in the world is because of these four autads.' Abdul wrote all this down, which is now available in what is called *Abdul Baba's Diary*.

'Are you getting all that I am saying? You, as someday there will be some crack man like Rabda here who might want to write about all this and that time, Abdul, for you and me, there will be hundreds of thousands of devotees coming sometimes every day, and we will be visited every day and they won't give me or even you rest, Abdul. Today they do not recognize you but tomorrow because of your proximity with me, Abdul, my crow, you too shall be worshipped.'

Abdul began to cry. He was a simple man. All he wanted was to serve his Master.

'Then there are four men who are below autads but whose function is very special but that is not to be written about and then there are three hundred people who are continuously reciting the Holy Quran day and night. Then you have seventy najibs who are meant to take on the suffering of those who are on the path but suffering, and these seventy najibs give those suffering a lot of solace. We have seven akhyars who serve the religion of God and, remember, God has only one religion and that is the religion of Oneness. Four thousand men and women whose only purpose is to spread the Light and do noble work. Then there are afrads, innumerable of them, who all day and night remember God, by whichever name they call God by.

'You have a naqib; twelve of them are collectively called nuqabas. Just as there are twelve planets, you have twelve saints or sages called nuqabas. Each naqib has the same characteristic of the planet he rules and also is aware of the pros and cons of the planet and also knows how to appease the planet and also knows all cures for an individual plagued by that planet. Now write this, Abdul, it is important.' Baba halted for a while. 'From Allah came about Divine Radiance or Light, also called nur. Then from Divine Radiance came about the innermost heart where Divine Revelation is experienced, which is also called sirr. Then from the inner heart came about the spirit or ruh, and the spirit is also called the musafir or traveller. Then from the spirit came the heart or dil and from the heart came about desires or nafs and from the desires came about the false I or false ego and the lower nature of mankind or even spirits. The nafs, or false ego or lower self, is called kafir.'

Caiz looked at Baba seated next to him.

'Baba, time out. I want to ask You a question,' he whispered.

'Why are you whispering?'

'I don't want to disturb You speaking to Abdul.'

'Oh Allah, if there is a spiritual hierarchy of idiots, my child, you will reign! How can Abdul hear you? This conversation took place exactly a hundred years ago. Ask what you want. Don't worry, we will return to what I was telling Abdul.'

'Okay. You said kafir means lower self, or false ego, right? But so many wars have been fought and so many killed in the name of fighting a battle of God and killing the kafirs or infidels. So who is a kafir?'

'Arrey wah, Rama Rama Rama, sometimes even you speak sense, mere Lal. Good point, you out-of-tune musician. Now listen, hear, be captivated . . .'

'Oh God, here we go again, why do I try to buy a cow for a glass of milk, I will never know . . .'

'Shaitan, listen. Kafir or infidel, in the true sense of the word, means somebody who does not walk the path of God. Somebody who has gone astray and is revelling and lustfully enjoying himself or herself on the path that is not the path of the One. Those who do all that which goes against the very tenets of God and basic humanity are called kafirs. The non-believer is called a kafir but a non-believer of good thoughts, good words and good deeds. Though for their own greed and manipulative reasons, some called all those who are not Muslims kafirs, which is completely untrue, non-Islamic and goes against everything Prophet Mohammed stood for. The Holy Quran itself acknowledges the ancient religions and advocates to those following the word of the Holy Quran that those who belong to the ancient religions are on the same path as those following the true philosophy and beliefs detailed in the Holy Quran and thus need no conversion or preaching. So how can every non-Muslim be called a kafir? Only those who go against all that is on the True Path, and that means those who do not walk the path of kindness, peace, compassion, tolerance, and universal brotherhood, are true kafirs and thus anybody following any religion, including Islam, can be a kafir or an infidel.

'Where I am concerned, the one following his or her lower self or one who has gone astray from the higher self of Oneness is a kafir and that is that. Did you understand a word I spoke, you frog?'

'Oh yes, I did, benevolent, calm, as calm as a child suffering from colic, Master.'

Baba muttered and abused and chuckled and then with a straight face said, 'Now listen to what I have to tell Abdul.'

'So, first and foremost, there are many avatars and there are various roles for all those who are held dear by the One.

'Remember, in the heart of each being reside four gems. The place of knowledge is in the chest and the enemy of knowledge is pride. The place of intelligence is in the head and the enemy of intelligence or reason is anger. The place of patience and mainly contentment is in the stomach and the enemy of patience and contentment is greed and doubt. The place of faith in God is in the heart, and the enemy of faith in God is untruth or seeking the false or being enamoured by glitter and the play of elements.

'Thus, most importantly, one needs to be careful of desires as once you have your desires under your control, you shall move into the region of the heart and once the heart is free from desires you shall see the radiance of your true spirit in your heart and then you will move towards the head chakras. From there you will see the Divine Nature, not only in yourself but in the higher self of all creation and then you will gain a glimpse of the One. Abdul, God is like the sweetness in sugar and the fragrance in flowers and just as there exists curd hidden in milk, and again hidden in curd is butter and hidden in butter is ghee, or clarified butter, similarly each being has to understand that God exists in everything and within oneself and all one needs to do is go within. Remember the famous Arabic quote which clearly states that the one who has recognized the Divine Light of Allah is the true believer and knower of the real truth.'

They were back in the cave. Caiz sat in front of the Fire while Baba spoke to various Energies and gave instructions. The sparks intensified and more went out of Baba and intuitively Caiz was certain a major calamity had taken place somewhere. Baba was angry. He raved and ranted and cursed and flung things and Caiz sat watching his Old Man and through it all it was only true love that he saw come forth from Baba. He was somebody who would not hurt a fly and would love the worst sinner too, as He knew the past, present and future and circumstances and the inherent goodness that lies somewhere in each being, no matter what. When there is complete Oneness, then who does one blame, judge or condemn?

Spirituality means to operate from the spirit. If you
operate from the spirit, you operate from Oneness and
if you operate from Oneness you can never go wrong.

'Mr Baba, why is there so much fighting over
God?'

'That is because mankind is essentially
a bunch of power-hungry chutiyas. They are not fighting
over God, they are fighting for power over others. So smart
businessmen brainwash those who are either vulnerable,
gullible, or bloody stupid, and create and misinterpret their
own version of the holy books. Thus there are innumerable
versions of the Vedas, Quran, Bible, Avesta, Granth Sahib,
as each one interprets the book according to his or her own
reality and state of mind and intentions. Those who fight in
the name of God have a special hell waiting for them and the
good news is that that hell is very secular. All those morons
who use God to create disharmony and hate and violence
and murders are all there, Hindu-Muslim bhai-bhai going
through such spiritual, emotional, mental agony for doing
what they did in the name of the Most Merciful and Just
that I cannot begin to describe it to you. When the lower self
realizes what it has done, the guilt, remorse, fear of what

awaits them for countless lifetimes on earth is frightful, to say the least.

'Rabda, there is a difference between spiritual and religious, and fanatical. Nothing wrong in being religious. You play a part there too. Religion is the stepping stone to spirituality. Your being religious can appease the lower gods but to make the One happy—our Lord and God, called the One, God, Ahura, Dev, Devi, Allah, whatever you want, happy—live and breathe through selfless love, compassion and Oneness, and that is being spiritual. Spirituality means to operate from the spirit. If you operate from the spirit, you operate from Oneness and if you operate from Oneness you can never go wrong. But sometimes a soul is too caught up with technicalities, rigidness and upbringing to go beyond religion, customs and rituals.

'Now what do I mean by lower gods? I mean those souls who have walked the path of rituals and code of conduct and prayers written down or handed down, generation to generation, and they are no longer in the physical body. When an individual leaves the body, the journey continues in another dimension. When somebody who has spent lifetimes reaching a level of comprehending the code of conduct and religious conduct, that individual can help so many to be initiated in the same, with the heavens hoping that the new recruits eventually imbibe all theory but move beyond customs and operate from selflessness and compassion.

'Each religion has a strict code of prayers and rituals. Five-times prayers began with Prophet Zarathustra. All Zoroastrians are supposed to actually pray five times a day. Zoroastrianism is the oldest known religion and the

Prophet is the first known Prophet of a religion. Hinduism, Sanatan Dharma, is not a religion. It is a way of life, thus the way of life doesn't have a Prophet. So a simple thing like praying five times has its different set of prayers, which Islam, the youngest religion, under the leadership of Prophet Mohammed—brought down by Archangel Gabriel, from the very breath of the Creator—too prescribes. The prayers may be different but they mean the same. The way of praying will be different, but the essence is the same. Imagine Zoroastrians and Muslims arguing with each other about whose prayer reaches first or is more powerful or heard by the One first. Religion teaches you what to pray with, the words to pray, the process of praying, the meaning of the prayers, the diction, the physical steps required while praying. Zoroastrians tie the sacred girdle called kusti around themselves, which has a particular prayer and process, while Muslims have to know how to stand, bend, kneel and prostrate oneself while chanting their prayers; religion will teach you even when to pray but no religion or elder can teach you how to pray. Words which come from the mouth reach only a particular dimension and create a very subtle impact on the body, heart, mind and aura. You may pronounce the words immaculately but if the words aren't coming from the very breath of your essence, the very sigh of your soul, then those prayers might as well be verbalized by an intelligent parrot.

'So, religion, customs and conduct are very important on the path, but it's an initiation on the path and it is certainly not the destination . . . very far away from the destination. What to do and not do and how to go about doing each thing, whether it is to perform prayers, religious ceremonies, the code of conduct—which would include diet, what to wear, what to offer, what to contribute—everything is laid down and taught by those in the body or those who serve as guides in the spirit dimension. It could have come from the sages or the religious heads or high priests and maulvis of every religion. Yes, the advantage of following these sets of rules and regulations are that the individual is walking a path tread by the seniors of that particular faith.'

'You said something about lower gods, Baba. Silly me, and I thought there was only one God.'

'I would advise you to refrain from using your lack of humour, it causes me spiritual indigestion.'

'Ya sure, this dream truly seems to be doing wonders for my sanity too. Okay, so lower gods.'

'The term "lower gods" is a way of describing those souls who have reached a stage of spiritual evolvement but due to their rigid mind frame have got stagnant in their growth and their divine journey has come to a halt, but that does not take away the fact that they are in many ways spiritual people, whose religious and ritualistic experience and knowledge is used to train those in the physical body who want to walk the path laid down by the Elders too. Please close your mouth; I can't explain such ancient truths with a man who looks at me like a goat, mouth wide open, virtually standing on one foot.'

'I shall practise silence. Go on, Master of the Universe and presiding Hero of this dream of mine.'

'So these souls have due to their rigid mind frame become judgemental. Yes, they are following the shariat or laws laid down by the elders of the community, but due to the knowledge and adherence of the ancient laws of religion, a certain rigidity, pride, ego, judgemental attitude has crept in and then formed roots moving very deep into the ragged sands of time, so these souls, who are without doubt very pure in a very rigid manner, have got stuck in the spiritual quicksands, which have known to devour the most spiritually evolved souls.

'As God can't be but the Highest of the High and there is only One God, some call Him Vithal, some Rama, some Kali, some Ahura, some Allah, the fact of the matter is that there are innumerable people following different paths and there are people who are kept in charge of those paths, and as they have an authority of some kind and degree, they kind of become like lower gods. Most of those who are rigid or fanatical about following the laid-down rules of dos and don'ts, usually after they leave their body, for whatever time frame they have to spend in the spirit plane, are assigned work to do; usually their work is to guide those in the physical body who are keen on following the shariat or the rules of religious conduct. The fact that these lower gods or spirits are so convinced that the path to God is only via the dictates and technicalities of what the holy books prescribe, they refuse to see that there is something far more subtle but more powerful—the easiest way to please the Lord and Master, which is following the path of the Higher Heart.'

'Lord, love a defrosted duck. Lower gods. Now comes Higher Heart. I mean, Baba, do You really spend time in conceiving these terms, 'cause I know You are a busy God and all that, so was just wondering.'

Baba smiled and put some wood in the Eternal Fire. He readied the chillum, took a few deep drags, handed it to

Rabda, who inhaled it a few times and this way the flaming fire was passed between the Master and the disciple, who refused to believe he was not dreaming.

'Before we come to the Higher Heart, we come to religion. Now understand this, Rabda, there is nothing wrong with being religious and following rituals and customs. Each ritual and custom came with a reason. Take ancestor worship. Remember each individual is an amalgamation of his or her karma and DNA. The karmic blueprint is decided by the individual's actions, thoughts, words, deeds and intentions of past lives and also the accumulation of this life. This decides the individual's present life journey in the body. The DNA decides the looks, personality, tendencies, health and a lot of other things. Good health and wealth more often than not comes from ancestors and karma combined. But how many remember ancestors apart from once a year during the prayers for the departed? Being in remembrance and gratitude towards one's ancestors is very important. How will parents feel if the children ignore and forget the parents? If the parents are not thought of or there is no gratitude shown towards them? After a while sadness enters the heart and soul of the parents and after a while blessings and prayers that naturally come from deep within the parents slowly start drying up. Do you have any idea how important the blessings of parents and grandparents are? Similarly, the ancestors too feel ignored, slighted, hurt, insulted and pained. The blessings stop pouring down and discord and disharmony begins to seep within the family living in the body. Remember, the ancestors may or may not send down ill will, but the goodwill and blessings and protection stop coming forth. Often ancestors are the guides to the family living on Mother Earth and the guidance stops. The family may have everything but not have peace and happiness in their lives or there could be continuous obstacles coming their way. Eventually, the family disintegrates; there are fights amongst the siblings, and after a point, no male heir to continue the family lineage.

'So usually what is advised is that the first roti or if that is not possible, rice, made at home be prepared in the name of the ancestors. A little ghee or clarified butter is applied and a piece of jaggery put on the roti or the rice and this roti is fed to a cow, black dog or a crow. So you might say this is a ritual and superstition. Do ancestors need all this or do they come down to eat all this? What is so special in a cow or a crow or a black dog? I agree. But the logic is this. When a family member prepares the roti, or it could be rice, and adds ghee and jaggery, the individual is supposed to keep the ancestors in his or her thoughts and feel gratitude towards the ancestors and also pray for the ancestors' well-being. Each family member is supposed to touch the food prepared for the ancestors, and by touching the food, every family member remembers the ancestors and seeks their blessings and prays for them. Now another family member might go and feed the cow, crow or black dog. While feeding the animal or bird, the individual too is supposed to wish for the ancestors' well-being and spiritual progress and also seek their blessings for peace and well-being amongst the family members living in the body. What one is basically doing is ensuring that every day the ancestors are being remembered and their well-being prayed for and their blessings sought.

If this ritual of making and feeding the roti, etc., was not indulged in, in all probability the family would not remember the ancestors every day and thus not pray for them every day and by not praying for them every day would eventually forget the existence of ancestors and thus be deprived of the blessings and protection that comes forth from the other world.

'Now why the cow, crow or black dog? Many families in fact feed each of these. Why? The cow is a non-aggressive animal and is often starving due to the lack of food available. The crow is not as beautiful, and certainly not as melodious as the other birds, and a black dog, because of the colour black is shunned. By feeding any of them, one is taking care of them, and blessings in the form of pure love that comes forth from them help the one feeding them and the family, past and present. The same way, Muslims feed the poor in dargahs in the name of their family, past and present. The blessings of the poor who are starving come from the heart. There are no ifs and buts about it. Clothe a man dying of cold and he will bless you from the heart as only he knows what it is to shiver. Provide medicine to the ill and the blessings come forth not only for you but your entire family lineage. The only thing is whenever you help somebody, do so in the name of your ancestors and your loved ones in the body. There is a downpour of blessings from ancestors and the one being helped and blessings go to the ancestors and you and your family.

'Now feeding the animal or bird or even another human being or an ant or fish or whatsoever—you may consider this a ritual but the meaning behind the ritual is spiritual. Each ritual in reality has a spiritual truth behind it. But if you were to just prepare a roti as a formality and feed the cow or bird as a formality then you have made it into a ritual or a custom or a superstition. And trust me, even the animal or bird will see the absence of love and care while you feed it. The world of the spirit and the world of selflessness operate from pure compassion and surrender.'

'Okay, I understand the feed-an-animal-or-a-crow part but what about all the sweetmeats left in the temples or places of worship as prasad. How does that help? I mean, many people are told to go to Hanuman temple and offer some prasad there, how does that help?'

'What do you mean by saying Hanuman? Is He your friend or something, maderchaud? Refer to Him as Lord Hanuman. Whenever you take the name of a God or Goddess or Prophet, give Them the respect They command. Nowadays you people refer to Gods and Goddesses as though they work for you all. Bloody idiot, give Them the respect and worship They command.' His eyes flamed but there was no personal anger, it was as though He was talking to countless people who have forgotten to give the place of Reverence to Those above. In seconds, Baba smiled and it was the most beautiful smile in all of existence.

'Your comprehension of basic facts scares me, Mr Rabda. I shall try to speak to you as though I am speaking to a mule with a very low intelligence quotient. Let us say you are asked to go to Lord Hanuman's temple and offer some mithai, sweetmeat. Usually it would be red in colour; on Wednesday Lord Ganesha would be offered green mithai, or on Thursday yellow sweetmeats would be offered. The colour depends on the governing planets of each day. Jupiter is called Guru, thus Thursday is called Guruwar (the day of the Guru) and His colour is yellow. Wednesday is Lord Ganesha's day, it stands for Mercury, Budh, the colour green, so the mithais too will be of the same colour. Do you understand, Rabda? Through your expressions you look like a very intelligent lamp post.'

'Very funny, Mr Lord God Master Sai, I understand.'

'Very good boy, so when you go to a God or Goddess's temple, you are meant to go with a particular coloured mithai and flowers as per the day of the week. Now it's not as though Lord Ganesha or the Master or Mother Mary or any one who you pray to and believe in actually eats or is hungry for the offerings. What They are hungry for is your love and devotion and remembrance. Every time you go to the place of worship, and when you go to buy the sweetmeats, or flowers, or candles, or attar, or chadar, or whatever, your mind is supposed to be on the One, for whom you are buying all these offerings. Then you drive or walk or go to the place of worship. Your heart should be in prayers and in remembrance of the One, you are going to worship. Then, in gratitude you place the offering to the One and pray for the well-being of your ancestors, family, friends, loved ones, all those in need of help, the abandoned, the weak, the meek, the distraught, the earthbound, all of creation. Then you seek the blessings of the God, Goddess, the Master, for yourself and all your loved ones and all of Creation. Then you leave.

'So what have you achieved? You have remembered your God or Goddess or Master that particular day and spent a bit of time in prayer, humility, gratitude, love and prayed for yourself, family, friends, those in need of prayers, ancestors, those earthbound, those passed over and all of creation, that is for animals, birds, fish, Light Workers and celestial, terrestrial and physical Light Beings.

'The ritual is to go and offer, but the reason behind the ritual is pure spirituality. Then your sweetmeat is distributed as prasad, holy offering, to all who come; the prayers you have done for all of creation are being distributed as holy prasad and all those who eat it partake of the blessings. Often we recommend the prasad to be given to the poor outside, as they are hungry, and once again in the name of your ancestors and your loved ones, you gain the blessings of the ancestors, those you feed and the One in whose name you are offering the prasad or sweetmeat. You may do it as a complete formality without any heart or you can make it a spiritual act. It all depends on you.

'When you go to a church or a dargah or a Shiva temple, you go there in gratitude and seeking forgiveness and strength to go through your lot with calmness and centredness and making your Master happy and proud of you for the manner in which you have gone through your lot. Does Shiva need milk and water and all the other things that are poured or applied on the Shivling? No. You pour milk and water and pray for the suffering, the anger, the violence, the heat to be abated in your personal life and for all of creation. That is the true reason for the offering to the Ling. Just going and washing the Stone, how does it benefit anybody? You might as well give the milk to a starving child. Why do you need so much milk? A few drops of milk in a container of water is more than enough, it is the prayer that goes with the cleansing of the Stone which is important. Remembering your intention in your prayer—one for yourself and your loved ones but most importantly for all those who suffer, all creation, to be cleansed of their suffering and the layers of darkness—is mandatory and needed. Do you understand or should I wash your fat head with various offerings?'

'God with a violent sense of humour. Hmm . . .'

'Nowadays, it has become fashionable to look down upon anybody who is involved in ritualistic worship. In Islam following the rules and regulations is mandatory, as if one can pray with one's heart and pray in the manner in which the Prophet or Holy Book has desired, then, bachcha, your spiritual growth is not only assured but also accelerated beyond the realms of imagination. Now, for a Muslim, the set of conduct is very clearly mentioned in the Great Book. Yes, very often the code of conduct is misinterpreted and used to serve to the advantage of those who have other agendas in mind, but the fact is that most of the code of conduct is written. Other religious books may or may not have rules and regulations written down in a detailed manner or they may have been lost over time, through many generations and centuries, thus there is conflict amongst people as to what is right and what is wrong. That is where mankind seems to fail. They have got stuck in words and forgotten the essence. They have got immersed in rituals and erased often the very heart of the Book.

'Thus the difference between a religious person and a spiritual person is simple. The former may or may not come from selflessness, compassion and Oneness. But a spiritual person will only operate from selfless love, tenderness, compassion and Oneness. You asked me what is going on in Shirdi or for that matter in any place of worship. Well, religion is happening. Spirituality is unfortunately mostly disappearing or has disappeared. Rituals are thriving but compassion seems to have been sacrificed. The places of pilgrimage and the temples and mosques and churches seem to be getting more and more regal, but the very essence that the Master, Prophet, God, Goddess represented, stood for, lived by, seems to have disappeared.

'All my physical life I have stood by the principle of Sufism or Bhakti, which is that poverty is the real richness as our true wealth and abundance is our love and faith in the One and His or Her love for us. Today my body is covered with silk, my walls have gold, I am fed and bathed in the fanciest manner, my very statue would be made of gold if people had their way. A fakir who walked about in torn clothes, begging for food, living in a dilapidated mosque which was also a temple and his home and refuge to all is now is clothed like a king, with all the luxury accorded to the very rich. When you see me in Shirdi do you see a poor fakir? Do you see the one who has spent his entire life in the body serving the poor, feeding the poor, caring for the poor and being one with the poor? If you were to get somebody who has never heard of me and bring him to Shirdi and see what is going on, would the person believe I lived my life in the most humble manner not because I had to, but because I wanted to live the life of a fakir or a yogi for whom poverty is godliness as for us, God, Allah, Vithal, Rama, Krishna, Shiva, Christ when in the body we resided with the poor by being one with the poor. Lord Rama was a king but lived such a long time in the forest in exile. Lord Krishna was a king but was born in a jail. Lord Christ was born in a stable. Why do you think They chose such a life? It is because the world and all its attractions for Them symbolize poverty, as it takes Them away from the One, while only the Spirit, the Realization of Oneness signifies royalty, wealth and abundance. This is the difference in religion, customs and spirituality.

'Today mankind goes through such trying times because in the name of God, innocent children of mine are killed. There is no greater sin in all of creation than to harm, abuse, slander, hurt, rape, kill, in the name of the One. Have you gone to sleep, bachcha?'

'No. A dead man who is dreaming or a man dreaming that he is dead can't afford to want to sleep.'

'I like your music. But as a comedian you really leave a lot to be desired.'

> You may pronounce the words immaculately but if
> the words aren't coming from the very breath of your
> essence, the very sigh of your soul, then those prayers
> might as well be verbalized by an intelligent parrot.

'Okay so now about this Higher Heart . . . or whatever You had said, Baba Sai.'

'Everything has a high and a low, bachcha. You have a Higher Self, which operates from calmness, pure love, selfless compassion, Oneness. Then you have the lower self, which operates from ego, selfishness, envy, sloth and all the other negative energies. Most individuals operate from the transit state, which is between the Higher and lower self, most of the day. A conscious effort is required to operate from the Higher Self. That is why every Master, every Ancient Book, advocates meditation, prayers, chanting, silent contemplation, to bring the breath to a state of calmness, which automatically makes the auras surrounding each individual become like still waters, which then makes the mind and heart function in tandem and harmony, and when all this happens Oneness resides in the individual for *as long as the breath is still and calm, the individual is still and calm, and when you are calm and centred, you are swimming in the Oneness Ocean* and your speech, thought, action will be calm and centred. You could operate from this state for a few minutes, hours, days—all depending on how important is it for you to flow in the same current of Oneness. Then of course something happens, a curt word from somebody, the food not prepared properly, the morning paper not delivered, the reading glasses misplaced, a phone call that doesn't arrive, whatever, and the breathing gets affected, calmness gets affected, stillness disappears, the aura becomes scattered, the mind and heart no longer are in harmony and then the individual starts to operate from ego and for survival, profit and loss, power and complexes. He reacts and speaks and thinks and acts like a child throwing a tantrum, and thus begins to operate from the lower self.

'You should know what it means to operate from both the Higher and the lower self. When you compose the divine music that you make through my blessings, when you are at work, you are surrounded by archangels and guides and the best of astral musicians, and you are one with the breath and nothing matters but creating the music. And then once the composition gets over, you don't know what to do with yourself. Boredom, emptiness, the void enters and then you start drinking, smoking, doing drugs, everything that is possible to glimpse the high you feel when you are centred or, in your case, when you are at work. Thus, your work is your salvation but the sad part is that for most people that very work becomes their sinking sand, as the moment you stop working, you don't want to be engulfed in the emptiness and void, so to recreate the centredness you experience or, for that matter, so many experience while at work or when involved with what they are passionate about, one begins to resort to various other things, shallow things, to recreate the magic of Oneness.

'You cannot recreate the feeling of Oneness through the drug or liquor store, nor from physical intimacy and pornography, nor from gossip and slander, nor from mindless distractions . . . the problem is that the feeling of Oneness comes when the breath is flowing calmly, when there is harmony between the heart and the mind, which automatically with the flow of prana or life energy or life spark in the right manner causes the auras to become still, and then you glimpse or breathe the fragrance of Oneness.

'So most often people operate from the midpoint of the Higher and the lower self. The problem with operating from the lower self is that you slowly start attracting lower energies towards you, and they slowly enter you through your scattered auras, and then slowly make you start doing things which are not really you. Most people aren't even aware that they are being worked upon or manipulated or being made to do things. The lower energies start to influence the individual according to their demands. They feed on chaos and darkness. This is the food and fuel for lower energies. Thus, they will ensure fights within the individual and around the individual. All scope for harmony slowly gets burnt down. The lower energies want to make you a vehicle to create disharmony and madness as that is their food and subsistence. They are present everywhere as the doors of paradise are shut to such energies and they roam about the fringes of creation, feeding off the uncentredness of all living beings. For them, the more the merrier, as there is more power in numbers. Most drug addicts are happy when they know another individual has become a drug addict. Most sex offenders feel comforted when they read that there have been more rapes and sexual abuses in the papers, as that makes him or her feel that he or she isn't alone and that there is a community that understands and empathizes with the individual. Thus, the lower energies enter the individual when the individual operates more and more from the lower self.'

'So what happens then? How do you get out of the lower self and get rid of the lower energies?'

'The first and clear way is to strengthen yourself. You see, the issue with the lower self and lower energies is simple. They make you feel all is well with you and that the other person or other people or the world is at fault. Thus, the person becomes judgemental and plays the victim card. I am a victim. I am not wrong. The world is wrong. The world is stupid. The world is senseless. I am right. You are wrong. Of course, when you are hanging upside down, you feel apart from you, all are upside down, you are the only person upright and seeing the world in the right way.'

'Babae of mine, I still do not understand this concept of lower energies?'

'You are so humble, my child. Though you barely understand any concept about anything, so humbly you point out each and every concept you do not understand.' Then Baba began to grumble, abuse and mutter under His breath. The most lyrical of bad words and swear words came out like an orchestra suffering from a stomach upset, all running hysterically towards the loo.

'So you know that you are the spirit in the body and not the body, right?'

'Sort of?' Rabda made sure he kept a straight face.

'One day I'm going to nail your two hanging round "sort ofs" to the floor. Bloody maggot!'

'Breathe, Baba. Operate from the Higher Self, Mr Sai. Breathe. Flow in the harmony of Oneness.'

Both the men began to chuckle. Baba Sai exhaled and began to prepare another chillum. Outside it was really dark. The sky seemed only to be dotted with stars twinkling bright. Rabda had seen so many shooting stars since his stay with his Baba here, but each time a star shot by, he gasped with wonder. He had never felt at home anywhere but in this humble cave with nothing in it, just the Fire burning and a rag on which Baba Sai sat; there was truly nothing else in the cave, but it had his Baba Sai of Shirdi, and Rabda realized eventually the only thing that could fill the gaping void within oneself is to be as close to one's God and Master. Only that mattered. Nothing else did. For Rabda, there was no place, either on heaven or earth, which was as precious, comfortable, perpetual as this cave where he sat with his Sai. Thus, the state of being is dependent not on material comfort, emotional and physical harmony or mental quietude, but eventually on how close you were to the One. It depends on how enveloped you and your aura are with the energy of the Master. Your state of centredness decides your state of being and essence. If you are in a state of centredness, then whether you have material comfort or not, whether you experience emotional and physical harmony or disharmony, whether you are in a good place mentally or not, nothing matters, as you are beyond being affected by all these things, as you have found your cave where your Master resides, and you are one with Him or Her. If you are centred, your world around you could be collapsing, but you would be nurtured and nourished by the Fire from the cave and the serenity of your Master's presence.

'My daft imbecile of a child is learning. Good. Yes, my son, when your priority becomes to operate from a state of centredness, it means you are operating from the state of the spirit. You are not operating from the body, the mind, the heart, the circumstances, the ups and downs, the prejudices and dogmas, the opinions and the comments, the praise and the slander . . . you are beyond all this, as the spirit operates from Oneness, as your spirit and each individual's spirit has come forth from the Lord and Master, and that spirit or energy or spark or floating divinity has come from the One and operates from permanence and Oneness. In permanence and Oneness, there is no duality and no harmony or disharmony, as when you operate from the Spirit, you operate from centredness and do not care about situations and conditions and circumstances. Your priority becomes to live so that you are no longer reacting to a situation or circumstance but you are observing, doing your duty, giving your best, but like somebody watching a movie, where you too are part of the cast and the not the main character.

'When you act from centredness and from the energy, you have dropped all pretences and all paraphernalia needed for shadow dancing. Now the problem is that most people think that as soon as they pass over or die, they automatically begin to operate from the concept of being energy rather than the body. That is so far from the truth. You see, the spirit is encased in three bodies. The physical, the astral and the causal. As I have told you, each person may have another name for the other two spirit or energy bodies, but the fact is one is encased in three bodies. So you have your essence or being, which is contained into the physical body. The physical body is contained in the emotional or astral body, which is contained in the mental or causal body, which wraps the spirit. When an individual dies or passes over, the physical body drops. The spirit now is encased in the astral or emotional body, which is encased in the causal or mental body.

'So when an individual passes over, it is not mandatory for the individual to work from the Spirit or Energy consciousness, as the individual is still encased in two bodies. Even there the individual will feel himself in a body, made of three elements: ether, air and fire. These three elements make the astral or emotional body. When the individual begins to operate only from the spirit energy, slowly the astral body starts getting weaker as the individual is clearing all karma attached to the astral body. So there too you are working out your karma, but that karma has got to do with the astral, or emotional, body. Maybe physically you are done with your karma, so you do not need to don the physical cloak. Now left are two bodies, the astral and causal.

'So let us assume you have worked out even your emotional baggage. Now you have no emotional or astral karma left behind. So you drop that astral body and now are left with just one sheet covering you from your true essence. That is the causal body, which is made of just ether. When you work out all your karma connected with the mind, thus having no physical, emotional and mental karma or desires, then you become one with the One, you then are Divine Prime Energy.

'So when a person passes over, it does not mean the person has moved on from operating from the body and is only operating from Oneness. The person is still caught up with the body and is still operating as a body rather than as the energy within the body. Now many times what happens is that an individual who has passed over still has too many physical cravings or the mind is so fogged with anger and lower emotions that he begins to try and satisfy those longings by using another person who is still in the body. So if an individual craves alcohol, he or she will try to look for an individual who he or she can enter and satisfy the incessant craving of alcohol. If a person wants sex, the same method is adopted. Also many want a release for their frustration and anger, or just want to spread disharmony and unrest as, for whatever reason, they feed off these emotions. They get stronger and more powerful when they can cause unrest and disharmony, so they seek a body to work off their frustrations and spread disharmony. These individuals are called lower energies and they operate through the lower self of another individual.

'When a person is not centred, when an individual is filled with hate, anger, ego or paranoia, these lower energies find that person a perfect nesting and breeding ground to spread their hate and venom. That is why prayers and silent contemplation is so important but most important is the realization that whatever takes place, the genesis of that issue is in some other lifetime and in some other body, but is carried forward till the experience is not gone through calmly and with wisdom.

'You had asked about the karmic clutch and how one goes beyond karma. Well, son, apart from charity and selfless giving, the other ways are through prayer, chanting and meditation. When you pray, chant, meditate, become one with the breath, the karma that clings on to the bodies is slowly burnt or washed away. It takes time and it takes discipline and it takes calm acceptance. What takes place with prayer, chanting and meditation is that either the karmic experience that has to be gone through via the dream state, where you go through the discomfort and the experience but via the dream state, or the load of karma is broken down to innumerable smaller sizes, where carrying the karmic weight becomes bearable and not back-breaking. Also prayers, chanting and meditation get you centred and that allows you to go through your lot with calmness, wisdom, and serene acceptance. So nothing has changed but your attitude towards the experience and thus you can go through your lot with ease and calmness.

'But when an individual operates from the lower self, the causal body, which is the outer layer, which envelopes the astral, which covers the physical, which encases the spirit, begins to get eroded. Initially small dots form on the causal body. Then slowly, the dots get bigger, as though there are holes or cracks in the aura. Then the holes begin to get bigger or cracks deeper, and if the individual is not calm, not in the process of centredness, prayers, chanting, meditation, affirmations, these holes and cracks only get bigger and there is no healing going on. With no healing going on, there is no protection. It is like leaving your home open, the doors and windows open, for anything to enter. When the mind is agitated, the vibration it emits begins to attract other energies with the same agitation or harmful intentions.

'Those energies begin to slowly enter into the astral body and physical body via the gaps in the causal body. The more unprotected the outer shell, the more erosion takes place till, like a gaping hole, it is an invitation for lower energies to begin boring holes into the astral and physical body. Thus the mental, emotional and physical body are prey to the lower energies and with more noise and commotion and anger and false pride and paranoia and anxiety and hate and suspicion, the hole gets bigger and becomes an entry point and breeding point for lower energies. These lower energies then begin to try and live out their base emotions and desires through that individual and also make the individual prey to their demands and their whims. It becomes more and more difficult to heal the person, as the person gets more and more into the power of these lower energies. And the worst part is, most people will not even recognize that something is wrong as most often it is brushed aside as stress and tiredness or bitterness creeping in, or innumerable other reasons. The poor person is then put on heavy medication and very often drugged for a while or for the rest of his or her life. Various medical names are attributed to those being controlled by lower energies. The best way to recognize these lower energies is that the person's behaviour is often normal and then suddenly for days on end gets more and more hysterical or negative and bitter and then again the person for a while is normal and the cycle continues.

'The best way to deal with this situation is to make sure the individual is sent lots of prayers and healing, made to drink charged water and made to eat food prayed upon. If the individual truly wants to get out of the grip of the lower energies, then prayers and visiting pilgrimage sites, shrines and the resting places of Masters are a must. Remember, when you go to a dargah of a Master, the attendant will always use for aura cleansing peacock feathers which have touched the Master's samadhi or tomb and then used on the devotees. Seeking the sun to cleanse your aura and praying to the sun to remove all the lower energies and darkness and the evil eye which clings to the aura and works within the individual is a must. Using God-given elements like charged water, fire meditation, sun cleansing, chanting, prayers, eating food and drinking water first offered to God, Goddess or Master and converting it into prasad and consuming only this sanctified food and water—all this goes a long way in once again healing the aura, cleansing the individual from within and outside and then fortifying the heart, mind, body and all coverings that encase the individual's very being. But the world has advanced to such a level that now all this is considered to be superstitious. However, this is the ancient truth; wherever there is good, evil will lurk close by. Where there is light, there will be a shadow. Where there is dawn, twilight is waiting to follow. Seek the Master's grace and protection each moment of your life and day. Whatever you do, involve your Master. Before sleeping, cleanse your hands till the elbow, feet till your ankles or knee, wash face, wash neck, gargle, and then say a short prayer for protection and sleep. Ask and plead with your God, Goddess, Master to keep you and your loved ones protected. When you wake up once again pray in gratitude and pray for protection. Touch your forehead to the ground thanking Mother Earth for everything and most importantly, for bearing one's burden. This should be the last thing you do before you sleep and first thing when you get out of bed; this should be mandatory. Seek the blessings of the Goddess and Mother Earth. She only gives and never expects or asks for anything in return. And most important, you disgruntled yak, make sure you are silent in the mind, heart and speech. When noise is less, silence begins to heal the individual, as silence means the element of ether, which is closest to the Divine Energy. When silence begins to grow within you, it begins to fortify the individual by healing the aura. The aura can be healed best by calm silence. Not angry silence, as angry silence is louder than all the sound in the world. Did you understand a word I said or are you just pretending to nod that big, thick, astral head of yours?'

'Brother, I have never wanted to wake up from this never-ending monologue of a Master who keeps talking and then preaches silence. Hmm . . .'

'Bloody basketball you are.'

Being in remembrance and gratitude towards one's ancestors is very important.

'So tell me, does mankind behave like the scum of creation only because of lower energies, those negative energies working on people?'

'No. Sometimes there is so much negative energy within the individual that there is no space for outside lower energies to even enter. An individual has the capability of being God incarnate or becoming the scum of creation. This ability only resides with mankind. No other species has the potential or ability to walk with the Gods or crawl into the depths of hell with Satan. The mind can be the harbinger of peace and sanity or the pit of depravity and madness. Thus, the individual can plummet into the abyss of decadence and he or she will be then ably helped by lower energies surrounding him or her. That is why it is so imperative to be calm, centred, silent, always in humble gratitude and spiritually always on your knees, with your forehead on the ground, in prayer. It is so important to be in prayer, I cannot emphasize this enough.'

'You mean most important to be centred?'

'Yes, crazy man, who keeps trying to kill himself.'

'You said somewhere, let the world go upside down, you remain where you are . . . stand and stay at your own place, meaning . . . stand calmly and do not let anybody ruffle you . . . look calmly at the show of all things passing before you.'

'Yes, and this can only happen when one is content with one's lot; remember, however simple this statement may sound, one of the pillars of spirituality and the cornerstone of happiness is the graceful acceptance of one's lot. Centredness is nothing but perfect surrender and being in glorious acceptance of one's lot . . . but after giving your hundred per cent to life . . . after embracing your lot.

'Where there is no centredness, then lower energies begin to breed, either within, or they crawl in from outside. The only way to go through life is to give your best and then leave the rest to Allah, God, Rama, Goddess, Master, the cosmos. Have you ever wondered why the neem tree under which I sat down, made some leaves, some bitter and some sweet? Neem leaves are one of the bitterest things created by the Almighty God. Bitterness often cleanses you of toxins that have collected within the body, slowly harming the vital organs in the body, slowly blocking the flow of oxygen, blood and prana, the very life force. But it is the very bitter taste in the neem leaf that contains life-enhancing qualities and flushes out impurities. When the Guru is involved, S(H)e can make some neem leaves bitter and some sweet. What was I trying to tell my people: that the leaves became sweet because I sat under the tree? No, you dehydrated mule. What I wanted to tell the people was that life is part sweet and part bitter. Even with the presence of the Guru, one has to swallow the bitterness that has ensued and perpetuated due to one's own karma. The rewards of free will used wisely makes

one's life sweet . . . thus life will always be bittersweet, and
to expect only sweetness is rather childish and petty. With
or without the Master, your karma is going to necessitate
what you are going to go through, and how many leaves are
going to be bitter and how many sweet. So the only wise and
commonsensical way of going through life is calmly, giving
your best, and leaving the rest to Him.

'Look at man. God created animals for various reasons.
One of the reasons is that the soul goes through each and
every species, every creation, till it reaches the stage of a
human being. The laws of evolution were first laid down
by the scriptures—that chap Darwin got that bit right but
everything else muddled up. The Vedas and the Shastras
clearly state that the soul has to go through eighty thousand
so and so number of species before the soul is clothed as a
human being. We have to experience all of creation and then
realize that only merging with the Creator matters. All else
is false. If the evolution of man was from animal to human
being, then why are there animals still around? If from apes
we evolved into human beings, what are apes still doing
walking around, scratching their balls and making funny
faces! Their purpose is over, is it not?

Evolution is all-encompassing. Man evolved from the
apes, starting from a cell then moving to a worm . . . my
eyes always fill up when I think of a worm . . . it reminds
me of you, my beloved . . . hee hee . . . and then evolution
progressed . . . but where we are concerned, evolution is not
of the body, but of the soul . . . to experience every species,
collate all experiences and then become a human being . . .
and see the way human beings are going about, fucking

everything that they touch, including even God's plan, by behaving worse than one with the most animal-like instincts, which are not even found even in animals.

'Why have human beings only taken the worst from their animal brethren? Instead of taking devotion, selfless love, faithfulness from a dog, mankind has taken the animal's inherent characteristic of barking and growling and doing all that is required for the stomach and a few inches below the stomach. How is it that mankind has taken the lower energies, which in animals is justifiable, survival energy . . . but in mankind they become lower energies . . . while completely ignoring the more divine qualities of the animal?

'You know of Abdul, right?'

'Yes, the one who served you for virtually the longest time.'

'Yes, Abdul was nineteen when I pulled him towards me. He came to me just after I came out of my three-day samadhi. He served me in the body, in this lifetime for twenty-nine years and then served me through my mazar and tomb for another thirty-odd years. He used to on and off write down all that I spoke to him about.'

'How come a book on that is not available?'

'That book contains my knowledge about Islam and Sufism and its tradition and the entire lineage. As I have told you before, if you were to read that book, you would never consider me to be anything but a Sufi and one who either was born into or followed Islam, and that is why the book is not as popular or most researchers do not give it the right importance. Anyway, you demented ape, stop disturbing me!

Let me take you to Shirdi and you can sit and hear what on and off I narrated to Abdul.'

'Mr Baba, I do not know much about Abdul, so could You take some time off from Your chillum schedule and at least tell me who Abdul was, etc.?'

'You worm, you have come to test my Godhood. I am now certain.'

'God with anger management issues, please either tell me about Abdul or then take me to Shirdi and let me see what I have to and then we can sit down and you can yap to Abdul and through the long sermons can speak about inner lower energies.'

'Bastard.'

In permanence and Oneness, there is no duality and no harmony or disharmony.

In a second Baba Sai and Rabda were in Shirdi.

'Okay, you can see yourself there, can you not?'

'Yes, I can. I look the same but I know this is the year 1889.'

'Yes, Abdul was summoned by me, twenty-nine years before I left the body, as I have told you, just after my first samadhi. He was earlier living with a fakir Amiruddin in Nanded. In a dream I told the Sufi to give Abdul two mangoes, which I had got for Abdul, and then send Abdul to me. In the morning the Sufi found two mangoes and realized he had to send Abdul to me. He gave Abdul the two mangoes and Abdul came to me as a nineteen-year-old lad.'

'You mean You told the Sufi Master and he just let go of Abdul.'

Baba Sai turned and looked at Rabda. It was a look that meant 'Is there a power in creation which can refuse me something?'

'Ahhh, obviously nobody can refuse the Sai Baba anything.'

'Why do you call me the Sai?'

'Arrey Baba, Sai is a Persian word for saint, sage, fakir, man of God, and Baba means father. If you were to come down on earth, you throw a stone and it will hit either a man who claims to be a man of God or somebody who is called Baba. I mean if I were to sit with a bandana on my head people would call me Baba too.'

'You are very funny, Rabda. Are people off their heads to call one and all Baba? And especially you, you make me laugh.'

'Anyway for me you are the Sai Baba. Many claim to be Sai incarnate, Sai Anksh, Sai this, Sai that. But for me, You, my chillum-smoking sage, who can give a drunk sailor a complex when it comes to either abusing or getting involved in a brawl—only You are the Sai Baba. Anyway, so now let us move on about Abdul.'

'You see it for yourself, you insect that reposes in cow dung.'

'Wow. Do you actually spend time formulating these slangs? . . . Okay, okay, let me observe. Shhhhh.'

And like in a movie unfolding in front of him, Caiz walked around Shirdi with Baba Sai. He saw himself as Rabda, the young lad who had committed suicide and with Baba's grace lived with Baba in Shirdi, in the astral form, doing as per the calling of Baba Sai. Even in 1889, Shirdi was virtually the same place as it was thirty years before when Caiz for the first time saw Rabda approach Baba, just moments after he had committed suicide. There were not too many people crowding around Baba. The band of followers from Bombay had not yet arrived. Baba's masjid, Dwarka Mai, was virtually a rundown place, with the floor still made of mud—on and off cow dung was used to smoothen and freshen the ground. The front of the masjid was open, thus rainwater and sunlight and wind and all the elements and the fury of nature were welcome, without prejudice.

Caiz saw Baba sitting with Mahasapati and Shama, smoking a chillum, when Abdul approached. He was a thin, young, tallish man, yet in some ways, still a boy. The moment he walked in, Baba smiled, looked at Abdul and said, 'My crow has come.' Caiz realized that the crow was being equated with things which were of the ordinary—things to do with the routine and mundane.

The first thing that Baba told Abdul was that the latter's role was to take care of Dwarka Mai and the lighting of the five lamps there, one lamp which burnt at Lendi Garden, called Lendi, as that was the place Baba Sai used to go to pass motions and where He would also sit with pots of water and He would sit and pray and sprinkle the water all over. Abdul was to wash Baba's clothes in the stream which flowed near Dwarka Mai and basically take care of all of Baba's needs. Baba Sai made it clear to Abdul that He would get nothing in return but the salvation of His soul and that when Abdul would leave His body, mud would be converted into gold. Even in the last decade of Baba Sai's physical sojourn, when the devotees came in droves, and money was given to Baba as an offering, Baba Sai never gave Abdul a rupee, though a lot of money was handed to Sufis and sages and the poor. Both Abdul and Mahalsapati were kept in poverty. This shows the high regard and respect Baba had for both these disciples. As for Baba, voluntary detachment from money was the highest kingship, as God was the friend of the poor or those detached from all material longings.

In the beginning Abdul would go and beg for his food and he was made to sleep in the stable near the mosque.

Caiz saw Abdul beg for food, sleep in his humble abode, take care of Baba, clean the streets Baba walked on, and later, decades later, often along with RadhaKrishna Mai, make sure that Baba did not step on stones and pig and cow dung.

Also, Baba made sure Abdul never ate too much. His instructions to Abdul were clear. Eat little and eat one simple dish, do not mix various kinds of food. Sleep as little as humanly possible. Embrace detachment to the highest degree with true love. And speak less.

Caiz saw Abdul sit at night reading the Quran and very often it was Baba who would open the Quran randomly and hand the Holy Book to the passages of the Quran loud enough to be heard by Baba. Often Baba would explain the true meaning of the verses and it would be dark outside, with just lamps burning, the Eternal Fire burning and Baba Sai and Abdul awake virtually through the night, with the soft whispers of the Holy Book being read. Sometimes Abdul would fall asleep and once even fell on Baba who was resting for a while and Baba tenderly woke Abdul up and with a smile told Abdul to continue reading. Abdul would sleep for a few hours and then work through the day serving Baba.

What Caiz realized that though there was so much proximity between Abdul and Baba, both respected and loved each other. For Abdul every word spoken by Baba was God's word and very often Baba would speak and Abdul would write in a notebook, the kind of book used by schoolchildren, with an ink pen. It was a beautiful sight. All through this,

Caiz noticed Rabda with both Baba and Abdul and very often Baba would tell Rabda to go and do His work, either in Shirdi or someplace far from Shirdi.

Baba made sure Abdul got married, but Abdul always worked for Baba. Even after Baba took samadhi, it was Abdul who cared for Baba's tomb. Till 1922 Baba's physical resting place was a dargah. It was later when certain devotees decided that Baba's tomb was a dargah and had no Hindu influence that Hindu symbols and paraphernalia began to be adorned near Baba's tomb; two years before Abdul left the body, the statue of Baba was placed before His very tomb and from that day onwards in 1952, Sufis stopped visiting Shirdi. The statue was given so much importance that, Caiz realized, unfortunately it overshadowed the very presence of Baba's resting place. Emphasis was and is given to the statue of Baba while His tomb silently watches everything. Abdul passed away two years later, in 1954, and till the end for him, life began and continued beyond with Sai Baba's name on his lips. For him, Sai Baba was God and beyond.

But all this Caiz saw in a flash. It was as though he himself was there but it all happened very quickly. He could feel Abdul's love and seva. He could feel Abdul's disillusionment at being relegated, as an evil necessity, to take care of Baba's tomb. The devotees wanted Abdul as they knew he had spent the longest time with Baba Sai, but Hindu–Muslim pettiness and ignorance sidetracked Abdul; Abdul kept serving Baba for thirty-years after Baba's samadhi and Caiz was certain that even now in the spirit dimension Abdul continues to serve Baba.

Caiz saw Abdul as an old man. Baba lovers would come to him for guidance and Abdul would pick up the notebook in which he had written all that that Baba said. He would pray to Baba and then open the Book and the answer would be revealed.

Also, Caiz saw Abdul sitting in the place RadhaKrishna Ayi lived; one day he was saying his prayers and the roof and wall collapsed and Abdul called out to Baba and though Abdul should have been buried in the collapse of the house and killed or frightfully injured, Baba Sai made sure His crow was safe and sound.

Caiz sat with Baba Sai while He explained to Abdul a few characteristics of mankind. Young Rabda sat next to Abdul, though obviously Abdul was unaware of Rabda's presence or the presence of the innumerable spirit bodies who listened to Baba Sai speak.

It was afternoon and it was raining outside. Baba Sai had just returned from begging for food from the five homes. He had got the food, mixed it, distributed it to the few who spent time with Him, and had eaten a few morsels. Then He sat with Abdul, while Rabda and other spirit bodies waited for Him to speak to Abdul. Caiz realized that Baba was never really alone. There were always spirits around Him, either hearing Him, receiving His blessings, awaiting instructions of spirituality or being given work to go and help those in need, in Shirdi and in far-off places.

Caiz sat in a corner along with Baba Sai and saw all this happening like a movie. It was surreal. A dream within a dream. Baba began to speak and Abdul began to write. Caiz realized that Abdul wrote down the gist of what Baba spoke but not necessarily the explanation or the language in which Baba spoke.

'Abdul, there are certain acts or types of behaviour which destroy all goodness. However good a human being may be, certain acts of mankind will put a severe dent into that individual's karmic record. Always remember that good acts form character and raise man's status. There are many types of behaviour and I am focussing on four of these. The first is animal-like behaviour, which includes attributes of lust, anger and greed. Then there is aggressive behaviour where a human being comes down from the status of being made in God's image and behaves like a wild dog, a wolf or any wild animal. Then there is satanic behaviour or pure evil: wanting the destruction of others or causing others pain for the sake of causing pain and spreading darkness. The fourth kind of behaviour is divine behaviour, with angelic attributes and conduct.'

Abdul wrote all this down but his points were concise. It was obvious that this book was meant for his spiritual growth and not once did he ever realize that it would be read by any other being.

'Abdul, a man who is not virtuous behaves like Satan, but an individual who uses his or her intelligence can use the power of free will and proper discrimination and can not only behave like an angel but become an angel. Each child of Allah should work always towards perfecting his or her knowledge of how to walk the path, should abstain from doing evil deeds, and wish well for all people. Everybody is equal in the eyes of God, Abdul, always remember this. No matter whatever name you call Allah by, there is no religion in God's eyes. God is One and everything has come from Him. Also it is very important to keep those indulging in bad deeds and those who are evil-minded at a distance. Avoid such people like the plague, Abdul. Remember this always. Allah is with all, those who remember Him and those who do not. He loves all. He seeks only love. Only true love and for you to walk the path. This way each child of God will live with honour, realizing the greatness of the Name or nama and that child will always be happy.'

Abdul wrote Baba's words down but he wrote them short and sweet. He wrote down Baba's words but often as he could not keep up with Baba's speed he did not write everything. But Caiz heard all and even read what Abdul wrote, and though Baba spoke in Urdu and Abdul wrote in the same language, Caiz understood all.

Then Baba looked around at all those who were present. He did not look at Caiz as Caiz was not present as Caiz, but as Rabda. These were words spoken by Baba Sai, sitting in Dwarka Mai. Abdul wrote all he could as Baba spoke, lost in His Oneness. Abdul had to often write down the words in short sentences. Abdul wrote Baba's words but stuck to mainly the essence and did not go too much into explanations. Sometimes Baba would speak slowly till Abdul wrote the words but Baba being Baba, He would then get lost in Oneness and then again His speech would take on speed.

'My children know that ignorance, deceit and using pretence are vices. Once again, I repeat, there are four kinds of characters or human nature: doglike, piglike, satanic or angelic. A dog is not judged to be bad because of its skin but because a wild dog symbolizes anger and the pig greed. Man can behave like Satan or like an angel. Each child's endeavour should be to elevate himself or herself above animal-like tendencies by using wise discrimination and wisdom.'

Suddenly Caiz was back in the cave. Baba Sai was smoking a chillum.

'Why am I here, Baba? I loved being there hearing You speak to Abdul.'

'Yes, I know, but you wanted to ask questions. So I will tell you exactly what I told Abdul and Rabda and all those who had gathered, and then you can interrupt me with your inane questions which I can explain to you, you constipated worm.'

'This dream seems to be getting more and more weird and verbally abusive. Hmm . . .'

> When silence begins to grow within you, it begins to
> fortify the individual by healing the aura.

'So my dear defective piece, let me reiterate one more time. A human being has the potential of behaving like an animal that predominantly focuses on lust, greed and jealousy. Then you have animal-like behaviour, with traits of anger and aggression. Then you have pure evil or Satan-like behaviour. And lastly you can behave like an angel or manifest divine angelic behaviour. So you have many people who have allowed the lower energies of animals to become their main character pillar. For example, there are people who are filled with anger. For everything they are angry. The first thing you can think of when that person comes to mind is anger. We all have to go through incarnating as every living species, and sometimes we have carried with us lower energies of a particular species along our spiritual and karmic growth, through various lifetimes, till even as a human being we continue to harbour and nurture that particular lower tendency or energy.

Thus many carry with them the lower energies of an animal, lower tendencies which form the main characteristic of the animal, as their prominent character trait. A wild dog is known for its anger. It has to survive and it has to mark its territory and guard its territory from other animals and thus it has to show anger as its strength—gnashing its teeth and growling and barking and charging every time another dog enters its territory. It will attack anything and anybody who comes in its way. Thus anger, which is needed for survival, becomes the main character of the animal. For the dog it is survival but when a man continues to harbour these tendencies it becomes nurturing and encouraging to lower energies. As I told Abdul, "It is the character which reflects the true nature, so the qualities of dogs and pigs are present in human nature, and when you allow these characteristics to dictate your life then it determines whether a man is satanic or angelic. If you come to understand that there is an inner controller or conscience, you come to assess your deeds and find out which of these four qualities influence and predominate over you."

'Now take the example of a pig. The pig is so greedy that when hungry, if there is no food around, it eats its own shit. We have countless such human beings around who are so greedy that to satisfy their greed they will do anything and everything. For that diamond necklace, for that house, for that car, for that increased salary, for that man, for that woman, for that post, for that power, for that fame, for that adulation . . . Shit can metamorphose into many forms, bachcha, and those who have no control over their appetite to possess, those who have no common sense to realize that eventually they are going to have to even leave their very body, leave aside all their material possessions, those who have no realization that the only true possession one has is one's God, Goddess, Master and that all else is transitory, everything one gets obsessed with which goes away from the reality of the spirit and is concentrated on the illusion of the gross or material, that individual is swimming in the shit pool of greed. Do you understand or not, maderchaud? Your expression is like that of a man whose marbles have been trampled on by a moving bullock cart.'

Rabda looked at Baba.

'Where do you get these analogies and expressions from? For a God, You are rather coarse, You know that.'

'Keep quiet and let me speak—if not you, there are countless who are present who hear this. So an individual can predominantly have one of the four characteristics. Yes, all characteristics are within each individual—anger, lust, greed, Satan-likeness and angel-likeness, each individual is capable of harbouring each and every characteristic, but eventually there will be one characteristic that rules. In your case, an overwhelming, intergalactic, beyond-the-propensity-of-comprehension amount of stupidity! You are as intelligent as that lamp post. Hee hee . . . How you make the angels laugh, just for that, you will be going to heaven.'

Rabda shut his eyes and sighed.

'I must truly love You to allow this dream to continue, as logically I should have by now have either professionally strangulated or electrocuted myself out of sheer boredom.'

Baba continued to chuckle and Rabda smiled. He loved the Old Man.

'Okay, so even you must have understood the four character traits that predominantly rule mankind. Please, appearances do not matter to me or the One. Be it a rabid dog, a filth-covered pig, or anything, that does not matter; what matters is that are you internally carrying within you a rabid dog, a filth-covered pig, a horrifying Satan-like appearance, or do you look like an angel within? Externals do not matter. Look at you, if externals mattered, you would have had a very hard life, as you look so distinctly funny. Anyway, you must remember that whatever you say, think, feel and do, it will come under one of the four categories, and it will begin to get nurtured and then slowly those qualities will develop and eventually rule the individual. If you encourage the fire of anger, you will become anger personified. If you do so for greed, you will become for this and many lifetimes possessed and obsessed by greed. Lust, jealousy, hate, all these will possess you and then that will turn you into one who walks the path of Satan.

'This is exactly what I told my crow, Abdul—if you win over emotions of lust and anger they will not be able to keep you under their control. The man is ordered to keep the dog of anger and the pig of greed and lust under control and subject them to the control of discrimination. Whoever does, that person's character will enjoy the state of bliss, so you see, Rabda, heaven and hell are in each individual's power. If in a dream you see an individual who resembles an angry dog or a greedy pig, you can be rest assured that person is a tyrant and is under the control of satanic influences.

'When you control the surge of anger, greed, lust, slander, gossip, it means you have begun to walk the path and you have begun to use the power of Oneness and God, you have begun to use the power of discrimination. In each individual there is a Divine Controller, and if you observe yourself and the way you live, you will realize which of the four characteristics rule you. What I told Abdul and what he has written is exactly the same. If you tie the pig of vices, then contentment, the fear of God, humility, wisdom, goodness and meekness will arise in you. If you become a slave of the dog of vices, then insolence, impurity, pride, boastfulness, ego, false humility, regarding others as inferior, and keeping close to base people will become a part of your character. If you keep this dog under control, then success, honour, greatness and forgiveness will arise in you, and all these good qualities will be your companions till the last. So you see, Rabda, each individual is eventually the Master of his or her destiny.

'Many people think that if they do not get angry or are not greedy, all is well, but even that is wrong. If you talk badly about others, you are behaving like a pig who eats its own shit. Every time you gossip, you behave like a pig eating its own shit. You may have anger and lust under your control but remember you still enjoy eating your own shit. When you deceive somebody, when you sell goods that are badly made, when you are cunning in your business dealings, when you destroy the faith in others or you destroy the faith in themselves, when you are not true to yourself or you deceive yourself which means you are not listening to the One within you, when you hurt somebody in order to make yourself look more good or in some way more superior, all these traits are also that of personal ruin and you not following the path of the angels. They are in their own way satanic behaviour. Abdul has written clearly what I told him: do not be under their control, triumph over them. If you truly discriminate, then wisdom, knowledge, learning, ingenuity, ability, good conduct, caring for the welfare of others, perseverance, all these good qualities will arise in you and will keep you company until the end of your life and will serve you well. Those actions which produce bad habits are called vices. So you see, bachcha, one has to decide which of the four categories you want to imbibe and become eventually. Chant your Master's name and, remember, many say that they cannot walk the path as they do not have a Guru. But, child, a Guru exists within each of us. That Guru is the Voice of Allah, God, Rama, Goddess. That is your eternal Guru.

'One day this man Balabhat came from Bombay and he kept pestering me to give him some mantra, some upadesh or what have you, something to initiate him and thereby make him my disciple and let me become his Guru. Do you know what I told him?'

Rabda thought hard.

'You told him to boil his head in mayonnaise . . .'

'Halkat . . .'

'Why would you call him that . . . ?'

'I told him, you rat suffering from herpes, it is not essential that one should have a Guru . . . everything is within us . . . what you sow, you reap . . . what you give, you get . . . there is no need for a Guru . . . it is all within you . . . try to listen and go within and follow the Voice and direction you get . . . each one of us should look within at our Self . . . that Self, that Voice . . . is the Monitor, the Voice that will lead you to salvation—this is what I told Balabhat.'

'Then why is it always said that without the Guru one cannot cross the sea of illusion and maya?'

'How many people operate from calmness and truly are honest with themselves about their flaws, strengths, weaknesses and limitations? The need to go within, be calm, should be a priority. It should be as important as breathing. When you go within and are calm and centred, when you accept your lot calmly, with positive surrender, with the full knowledge that you have given your best and now nothing more can be done, so let the Lord's will be done and accepted gracefully, then the individual is capable of hearing the Voice within and that Voice will guide you calmly, without favour or anger. The need to go within and come from calmness and not from reaction should be predominant and then you will hear what you need to, be guided and then go move on the path. *But how many people are centred and have embraced their lot gracefully after giving their best? How many do not live a life of reaction but of calm action? How many want to come from the only need of making the Lord and Master happy and proud of them each moment of their existence?* When you come from such a predominant need of calmness, the Guru within will emerge. That is why for most people a Guru is mandatory but for those who truly want to walk the path and are one with their breath and their calmness, the Guru's voice is heard.'

'You mean the Guru awakens?'

'You bloody idiot, the Guru is always awake. The man or woman who all his or her life has lived like a chutiya, but now wants to walk the path, begins to for the first time hear the Guru.'

Baba began to abuse and rant and rave and Rabda sat down, back to the cave wall, making another chillum, enjoying his God go ballistic.

*So the only wise and commonsensical way of going
through life is calmly, giving your best, and leaving the
rest to Him.*

They took a walk. It was a strange walk as neither of them touched the snow while they strolled about; they neither felt cold, nor did the breeze envelope them, it was silent, but not a stagnant silence, as whenever Baba touched Rabda, the latter could see scores of astral beings seated in prayer, and Rabda realized that each being was praying in his or her way the prayer closest to his or her heart, some chanting Islamic verses in gratitude to Allah, some chanting the Gayatri Mantra, some saying the Avesta prayers, some asking Mother Mary to bless every living being; Rabda could hear the Japji Sahib of the Sikhs, he could hear Buddhist chants, Native American songlike prayers, Jains praying, those who did not believe in organized religion praying to the One, it was like every prayer that was every penned, prayed or said for the glory of God, the peace of all beings, seeking protection for mankind and every living being that breathed, for the well-being for all those, from the past, in the present and those to come in the future, was breathed to the One, all at one time, and Rabda could hear it all and yet hear each one praying singly and it was strange and surreal—the perfect symphony, an orchestra in unison, a musician, as well as part of the ultimate rock band.

Rabda was so overwhelmed that he knelt, shut his eyes and prayed, strangely not for himself but for every being in the physical dimension, wherever the being was in, whatever part of the Universe, for those on the spirit plane and most importantly for those in between.

Baba made signs, different signs, in various directions and each time He made a sign a blast of light emitted from Him and travelled in that direction.

All Rabda hoped was that if this was a dream he never wanted to awaken from it and if this was real he never ever wanted to go back to his body. If death was this beautiful, he prayed that each being in the physical dimension would for once and for all live in a manner that would bring them to this state of serenity and purpose.

They returned to the cave. Baba was aglow. Sparks emitted from Him and disappeared. So many entered within Him and merged. Rabda realized how insignificant his life had been. There was so much of peace to spread, so much of Oneness to share, so much of love to be filled with, but what a hash he and most people made of the blessing called life.

Baba prepared the chillum and they smoked. There was nothing to say. Rabda could not get the image of the countless beings all in prayer, praying for the mercy of all, the well-being of creation and the glorification of the One.

It seemed like a fraction of a second or an era, Rabda was not certain, but Baba smiled, and Rabda realized that all of the splendour accumulated on earth and in heaven paled in comparison to the Old Man's smile. You knew you were safe. You knew all was well with the world and in heaven. You knew you belonged. Most importantly, you knew there was no duality, it was all Oneness.

'Rabda, there are a few simple truths. I have said this time and again. I will say it once more. The first most important truth: I am not a jiva or creature. Most people identify themselves as the being they are contained in. A spirit in a man's body identifies with being a man. A woman identifies with the feminine aspect of her being. A dog identifies itself as a dog but, Rabda, anything, anywhere, that lives is pure atma, a part of the prime atma called the param atma. The individual is not a man, woman, animal, bird, insect, it has taken the body to work out its karma and its spiritual evolution. Each one is a vibrant being that has come from the Source, and thus nobody is a creature or a jiva but we all are the essence and part of the One. You are Light. You are one with the One as you have come from the Source, Allah, Shiva, Vishnu, Brahma, Goddess, whoever you bow your soul to. Remember, you have come from the Almighty thus each being is God waiting to realize himself or herself.

The second eternal truth is that I am not the body and the greatest fallacy is that the body is the soul or the individual. Until you get into your very odd-shaped head that you are not the body but the spirit in the body, you will always be entrapped within the workings of the five elements and karma. The first step to walk away from the cacophony of duality and karma and illusion is to realize that you are not the body but you are the spirit within the body. So you are not a creature and you are not the body. When you stop identifying yourself with your body, you begin for the first time to give your true essence the power and the freedom to explore the Oneness and the Source that you and each living being has come forth from. The moment you drop the illusion that you are the body, you begin to give power to your very soul to soar to the Source. Otherwise you can say every prayer ever written, but till you acknowledge and live this reality, that you are God's essence within the body and thus you are not the body, thus you always were, always are, and always will be, that nothing can taint you, pollute you, destroy you, that you are purity personified in your original state, and peace, divine joy and power make up your original state, you will always wander about like a mad musician in the by-lanes of bondage.

'The moment you identify yourself as a spirit His Impression—you give yourself, your mind and your very essence the freedom to soar heaven-bound and dive deep into the very depths of your being and Original Source.

'Please do not stare at me with your mouth open, Rabda. Thank you. Now comes the third greatest illusion, which is that God, the world and jiva are different. Each being comes from the Source. From Allah. From Vithala. Be it an archangel, be it an astral being, be it a dolphin, a dog, a worm, a carpenter, homemaker, the Pope or of course an out-of-tune musician who jumbles up even a straightforward suicide. The world, everything ever created, comes from the Source, thus everything that has come originates from Shakti or the Almighty. Your hand is not different from your body, just as your leg is not. Each limb belongs to the body. It is separate but part of the whole. There is no duality. When you reach a state of God-realization, you come to the conclusion that everything is one.

'Thus you come to the fourth reality that I am God, or the fourth illusion that I am not God. When you realize that God, the world and every creature are one, and you focus on the spirit within you and not the body and you do not identify yourself as a creature or the body, you eventually, after continuous chanting, breathing, meditation and centredness, come to the realization that I am God as the spark within me is from God, and if the spark has come from God, then the spark too is God and the spark and God being one, you too are God. Though frankly, looking at you, Rabda, I truly want to change this philosophy, but what to do? God prevents me from changing His Reality.

'Thus the individual comes to the conclusion that everything has come forth from him or her and that you yourself are the Creator and thus I am God or Anal Haq. When you go truly within, the one who breathes, the body to which the breath enters, is exhaled through and the very breath all become one. There is no difference in the one breathing, the body absorbing and exhaling the breath, and the very air being taken in and breathed out. The purpose of your prayers should be that the one who prays, the One to whom the prayers are being recited, eventually all become one. Who is then praying and who is being worshipped, all slowly fade away and just Oneness prevails. Of course, I am not saying all this comes easily. It comes first and foremost with the grace of Allah or the grace of the Master but without acknowledging these realities, one is not swimming in the ocean of Oneness but one is drowning in a pool of duality and piss.'

'Aww : . . your choice of words sometimes leaves a lot to be desired.'

Baba again began to mutter under His breath. Rabda heard beautifully pronounced words not found in any of the sacred texts but from Baba's mouth they sounded more holy then all the texts ever scripted.

'Of course, without true realization if an individual claims he or she is God, problems begin as the person starts deluding the consciousness of realization. Some people can predict the future, some can out of air procure ash or a gold watch, some can see exactly what is present countless miles away, some can heal others, all these are slide shows, these are not remotely close to the real Film. God-realization is like acres of a rose garden. You cannot prevent the fragrance from reaching you and you cannot not see the ethereal dance of colours coming forth from that ocean of flowers. You cannot fake all this. You cannot be partially pregnant.'

'Hee hee . . .'

'You finding something funny you defrosted swine!'

'Partially pregnant . . . where do You come up with such terms, Baba? You are too funny!'

'I will thrash your nose into a straight line, then tell me who is funny, you blasted idiot. Anyway, shut up and listen as I am not talking to just you.'

And Rabda saw the cave filled with countless souls. All looking at Rabda with exasperation and resigned to him disturbing the Old Man who now was grinning from ear to ear.

'Now the fifth point is very similar to the above points but it has a little difference which is really important. You may have come to the conclusion that you are the spirit and you are not the body, but it is important to also know that the body is not spirit and thus it is temporal. So the fifth reality is that this body is not the soul or being in the illusion of not knowing that this body is not the soul. Why is this important? You may know you are not the body, but it is important for you to realize that this body is not the soul, and thus it will decay, it will age, it will fall apart, it will be besieged with illnesses, as when that knowledge seeps within your being, your identification with the body dies completely. Otherwise you may believe that you are not the body but your identification with the body still remains and it is important that the identification with the body dies as then and only then will you be free from the clutches of all which is temporary. Thus, as important as the knowledge that you are the spirit is the knowledge that the body is not part of you and not part of the permanent you, or the soul.

'And the last important reality or knowledge you have to ingrain within yourself, you exhausted migraine of a being, is the fact that God, the world and jiva are One. Once again this may sound repetitive but I cannot emphasize it enough. You may intellectualize this but it is important that you live with the realization of the positive knowledge that God, the world and each creature truly are One. It is important. Do you understand? Every time you believe in this Oneness Reality, you slowly start to know for certain that God, the world and you too are One. It reinforces this reality.

'A human being can keep praying but till these few realities are not embraced or illusions are not breathed away, true spiritual growth will not begin. Yes, you can be a very decent human being, but that means you will reap the benefits of your good deeds as a human being. However, that does not necessitate that your true spiritual journey has begun. Remember, who is a spiritual person? The one who believes he or she is the spirit and not the body, thus believing that he or she is from the One, thus acknowledging that he or she is the One, thus understanding clearly that God, the world and every being, including the individual, are One. Thus, when you call a person spiritual, the person should meet these requirements. Or else, call the person religious. Call the person a good, decent human being. Call the person still a work in progress. Spirituality cannot enter the picture till the very tenets of being a spirit are met and those will not be met till the realization that being One with all, including the Maker, has not taken place . . .'

'Yes, yes, I got it. You cannot be partially pregnant, hee hee . . .'

Rabda grinned. Baba laughed. The spirits let out a collective groan.

Always remember that good acts form character and raise man's status.

'So Mr Baba, I forgot to ask you a very important, interesting . . .'

'Idiotic . . .'

'Irrefutable is more like it, but here's what I wanted to ask the other day, or at least it seemed the other day though now I am not sure whether I have spent days or moments with my God with a very liberal vocabulary, can I ask, because with all these sparks leaving You and entering You, I wonder how You can keep a tab on what is going on . . .'

'Ask, ask, ask, ask, and get it done with.'

'Okkkkaaay. So here goes. You said the Guru is not mandatory for one to merge with the ocean. But You have always said and apart from you and all the ancient scriptures, and other Gurus have said that, an individual can never see the Light, as the individual is too busy to bother to remove his or her head from his or her rectal opening . . . which henceforth to be referred to as the bum.'

'Rabda, my darling child who should have been quickly strangulated at birth! I never said that a Guru is not mandatory on the path of the spiritual journey and to merge with the One. In fact, I said without the Guru nobody can reach the One.

But if you only listen rather than hear, you will realize I said that an external Guru need not be mandatory. The Eternal Guru is within each one of us. The Voice is the voice of the One. That Voice comes forth from the depth of the Eternal Womb. That Voice is within every living being but it is buried under the myriad, oh, for crying out loud, myriad here means a heap or multitude of karmic dumping or baggage. Thus it is not simple. In fact, it is very difficult for an individual to clear that vault or dumping ground of karmic give and take, sow and reap, stagnating needs, and then there is the subconscious clutter which most people are not even aware of, what is quietly slipped into that unseen vault. Then there are the conscious reactions to everything said, unsaid, seen, unseen, heard, unheard, spoken and unspoken, done and not done and of course there are lower self-interpretations and a lot of things that cover the Guru. Thus, to be able to see and hear the Eternal Guru within requires great discipline, unflinching focus and an attitude of "I'd rather die than not reach the depths of the internal ocean, get the oyster and yank the bastard away to find the pearl."

'So bachcha, though the Internal and Eternal Guru are always with each and every living being, not many have the focus, the dedication, the stamina and the gut-wrenching need to find and embrace the Guru within. Thus, it is better and safe and easier to be guided by the external Guru, as very often that external Guru has all the fucking time in the world to answer questions from suicidal, evolved maggots in the unconvincing disguise of human beings. Anything else you would like to ask, my darling son who suffers from spiritual vertigo?'

'Ya sure, that sounds groovy coming from a Master who went about thrashing every known and unknown person in sight when He was in the body. I want to ask You a simple question. Explain it to me as though I am a three-year-old child, spell it out as though I am . . .'

'Rabda, you know I can convert you into any of the thousand species I have at my disposal so if you do not get to the point, I shall make you into a point of example for decades to come . . .'

'Hmm . . . spiritual tyranny . . . ooookkkkaaay . . .' and in the tone of Amitabh Bachchan in the quiz show, Rabda looked at Baba Sai and inquired, 'Aur mera agla sawal'—for those not conversant in Hindi—'My next question' . . . Why have You said no to fasting when every Guru insists on sleeping less, eating less, talking less. I mean, what's with all You people? So basically walk around life, looking like a sleep-deprived, dumb zombie who is on a diet.'

'Hey Govind, hey Gopala . . . reham kar . . . okay, so in brief I shall explain to you certain truths about spiritual growth. These truths are present in every spiritual group; be it Sufis, yogis, monks, ancient lamas, all Perfect Masters, or every prophet, They have embraced certain rules. Yes, they have been written and followed like a path amongst Sufis for centuries now but the fact is that each and every known spiritual group or organization has this notebook of dos and don'ts and most of these books read the same.

'Abdul and countless Sufis came to me before 1910—for many Sufis, I was either a wali, pir or an aulia, and to some a hazrat and to some a qutub—these are all designations of spiritual hierarchy and in reality did not make a difference to Me. I am a servant, child, disciple, servant, friend, lover of God, Allah Tallah. You can think I am one of these or all of these or have a different interpretation of my relationship with Allah, that does not change the fact that S(H)e is my be-all and end-all.

'For these Sufis and yogis that came, the first step towards clearing out a lot of dirt or to unblocking passages and openings in the astral body as well as the physical body, was to fast, sleep less and talk less. For Sufis and those on the path, like monks and lamas, these things are mandatory. Yes, once you reach the top of the mountain nothing matters. A Master can eat all day or talk all day or seemingly sleep all day, He is beyond matter and the laws of cause and effect and the five elements and the laws of the five elements that rule earth. But as long as you are still climbing up the path, there are certain guidelines. So I used to allow Abdul to eat very little, eat one simple dish, no mixing of too many types of food, and sleep for a short time. I would tell Mahalsapati and Shama to make sure I did not sleep. We all would be awake till late in the night talking, praying, joking, so that sleep was kept at bay. Anyway, about sleep I will talk later. Now let us focus on food.

'So if you are on the path you must abstain from very heavy-to-digest food and also a large quantity of food, as food is made up of five elements and those five elements are governed by the law of gravity which shall drag the soul down rather than let it soar or it will block the passage one needs to go within the depths of one's very being. The body is working overtime to just digest the food and thus sleep comes about. So by eating too much you tend to sleep too much too.

'But for a common man or woman, somebody with a family to take care of, somebody who needs to travels to work, works all day, travels back, then takes on home responsibilities, how can I advocate fasting? The individual has so many responsibilities and thus needs to have all the strength to meet those responsibilities. Being out in the world requires physical strength and stamina. I cannot allow my children to fall ill or get weak and then not be able to discharge their responsibilities. Thus, it is important that the child eats well, though not eat as if food is disappearing or finishing every possible thing cooked, just because there is food. Eat moderately, eat slowly, eat well, but never overeat. Eat how much you truly require. But for a householder I will never advocate fasting. On the other hand, for those on the spiritual path, fasting is mandatory.

'The point is, how come my children only listen to and insist on this particular point—that Baba Sai made clear, not to fast, and don't obey the countless other things I have told, advised and insisted on? Everybody uses me as an excuse not to fast. How come nobody uses me as an excuse to not lie, not hurt, not cheat, not gossip and slander, not deceive, not manipulate, not steal, not usurp? How come nobody says, "Baba Sai has said do not fast and also do not hurt others, and be mean to others, do not backbite and do not simply fight when one can keep silent and with dignity speak one's mind out"? How come only "do not fast" is so sternly adhered to? That is because man likes to only listen to what suits him. They will hear everything but listen to what suits them. As it suits everybody to go and stuff their faces with food and reduce the food stock of the world, my maxim, "do not fast" is remembered and followed by all while the rest of all that this Old Man said is clean ignored.

'Eat to nourish your body and not to fill your stomach as, though the stomach is barely as big as your fist, God in His infinite wisdom made the stomach elastic, so it can accommodate twenty times the quantity each individual really needs. When I said, "Do not fast", I also said, "Eat enough to nourish yourself and not to kill yourself with food." Do not make food an obsession as otherwise most of the time your body will spend in trying to digest that food, while God in all His Glory awaits your one-point attention and focus. Can you meditate or pray with a heavy stomach? Can you give your very best with a heavy stomach? No. And of course, I forgot to mention that try to avoid having sleeping pills mixed with vodka. That makes you most often earthbound.'

'Ya, right!'

> When an individual controls the surge of anger, greed, lust, slander, gossip, it means he or she has begun to walk the path.

'So, Baba, before 1910 there is hardly anything recorded about what You said and did. Why did You not insist on all that You said to be recorded?'

'Everything is recorded, bachcha. Everything you say, do, think, feel, everything is being recorded. The advancement in the field of all your worldly technology is at least a few thousand years behind the technology of the spirit world. Everybody is so fascinated by this instrument you call the phone, which you can use wherever to communicate with whoever you want at a moment's notice.'

'Ya, right! Have you ever tried to communicate when you are in the lift?'

'I know. So many times I have had to change frequencies to make sure your talking dabba, or box, works during times of emergencies. But we have always been able to communicate from one part of the Universe to another, just by thought waves. You people are using electronic waves to transmit messages. We used thought waves to do the same and no carrying things, no charging the dabba, no paying monthly charges. We think of somebody, that person connects to our thought waves, we communicate and that is that. Then this technology where all information is available at the press of a button . . .'

'The Internet. Say it ten times, Baba. Inteeerrrrrrrrnnnnneeeet. Ten times, say it.'

'I ammmmmmmmm goooooooinnnnngggg to brrrrreeeeeakkkk your head. So yes, this Internet, though it should be called the dangerous web of technology, is available to you poor natives of the earth now. We have the akashik records where everything said, done, thought, felt, by every, by any, being is recorded automatically. Thus, from the beginning of time till now, your journey from a worm to this present form is being recorded.'

'I hope the manner in which certain God incarnates talk to Their loved ones too is being recorded.'

'So, you rat with three kidneys, listen now, we are always and will always be ahead of the physical dimension. How do you think you all have technology? That is because the spirit guides, who work on advancement for earthly purposes grace those working in the field of technology. For that Archangel Gabriel should be thanked. All forms of communication are done through my friend Gabriel. S(H)e is the voice of God and technology for the sake of communication comes via the voice of God. You wanted to know what was recorded, then go meditate, go within . . .'

'Ya ya ya, breathe, get centred, go within . . . I sometimes think all this breathing-sheathing, centred-bentred, meditate-sheditate, is all one big bloody con.'

'You, my disgruntled, everything-challenged yak . . .'

'Ya, ya, it is all about the breath, baby . . . Anyway, so

You spoke about the stomach yesterday and that how God in all His groovy intellect forgot to make the stomach non-elastic because if S(H)e had made the stomach non-elastic, millions of our poor children and brethren would have got food to eat, as people would not have been able to eat till they dropped dead.'

'Maderchaud, you think people are dying of hunger because there is no food to eat? Nonsense, people are dying of hunger not because there is elasticity around the stomach but because there is no love in the heart of most humans. There is enough food to feed everybody. The problem is there is not enough love and consideration to feed everybody. Anyway, once in a while you speak sense, so listen to me about the mind. I have explained it to Abdul so you might as well be taken to when I spoke to him; he has recorded it too.'

'Ohhhhh, those groovy black-and-white flashbacks. Okay, Mr Baba, beam us down . . .'

'I want to beam you into a volcano now so badly but I shall restrain myself. Control of the mind is very important for all, and with you around, you take the concept of the control of the mind to another dimension.'

'Am all ready and packed, Babae, beam us down.'

Baba began to curse and mutter under His breath but there was the most beautiful twinkle in His eyes.

Once again Caiz and Baba were back in Shirdi. It was in the afternoon. Caiz realized it was wintertime as there was mist everywhere. It was cold outside but Dwarka Mai was warm with the blazing Fire that burnt within eternally. The flames of Dhuni Mai were vibrant. Baba Sai sat facing the

Fire, while Abdul and a few other Sufis sat near Baba. Caiz saw Rabda sitting in a corner, looking at Baba Sai. There were innumerable spirit bodies all looking at Baba, hearing Him speak. Abdul was jotting down words spoken by Baba.

'So now we speak about a very important aspect of spirituality. The function of the mind. In the name of Allah most beneficent and merciful. Allah says, "We have created spirits (djinns) and man only for the purpose of worship. We have granted him the kingdom and the strength to conquer it. We have also given him the body, hands and feet, with the intention that he should enrich this world. In this way, he pays our debt and becomes our true devotee. In this way, like the Emperor, he serves the world and Allah."

'One must understand that the intellect, or the buddhi, is like the prime minister, or wazir, while the body, the hands, the feet, other organs are like servants. The heart is the treasurer, so that greed and envy should be allotted the work of spying so that you will be able to know about the theft of wealth and you will be able to attain your purpose. Now the brain of every human being is divided into two parts. The front and back. The front part of the brain is the receiver. It receives all information and messages and thus it plays the role of the reporter, or the one who receives and transmits information. The front part is thus for receiving and sorting out. You need to calmly receive and then by using your intellect decide what should be kept, what should be stored, and what should be deleted.

'The second part of the brain is like a treasurer, a protector or the memory vault, like a telegraph officer or an editor. A time will come when mankind will have machines that will be very advanced, but there is nothing more advanced than the mind and intellect. The body is the most advanced instrument every created by Allah, thus respect the body and the functions of body, which include the mind and the heart.'

Caiz sat near Abdul and saw Him jotting down a few sentences, the main gist of what Baba wrote, but usually never the explanations.

'So as I have told you, the intellect is like the wazir, or the prime minister, who governs the administration of the kingdom and thus makes all decisions that are for the well-being of the kingdom. But he should be alert, just, and have his priority very clear, which is to run the kingdom of the Lord, the King, in the best possible manner, in a calm and just manner. If the wazir is not calm and just, then the decisions taken will bring about ruin to the kingdom, which is happening everywhere.

'The wazir should be able to present and alert as there are a lot of enemies waiting to destroy and conquer the kingdom. There are many enemies of the kingdom, mainly anger, greed, lust, jealousy, sloth and the intellect. The wazir should be able to boost the morale of the obedient and nip in the bud all rebellion and destroy the enemies so that the kingdom flourishes.'

And in an instant Caiz was back with Baba in the cave.

'So what did you understand?'

'That often, You can be very boring and to the point.'

'I was surrounded by Sufis and seekers, not out-of-tune musicians filled with alcohol and sleeping tablets, thus one must speak the language of the listener.'

'Okay, whatever. So will You now speak in normal language about the mind? All this wazir and prime minister, and front and back of the brain, what do I do with all this? Get to the point, my Babae.'

'Get to the point, the idiot says; that should be easy, drill another hole in his anatomy and that will be the point.' Baba muttered to Himself and made the Fire flame further. 'So, anyway, the point is that the mind or intellect holds the key to the kingdom. If the mind is kept vigilant, if the intellect has sight of its priority, the empire will be ruled wisely. But if the intellect is scattered, and the individual is not aware of his or her priority—and being unaware of one's priority is like travelling without knowing the destination, the journey's route, the travel conditions, the weather conditions, the places of halt—the journey can become very chaotic and exceedingly cumbersome.

'The mind is besieged with information and subtle and direct impressions that need to be first calmly collected, then what is important needs to be sorted and, very important, what is not needed needs to be cleared off immediately. Most people are not in control of their minds or intellect. Most people are slaves to their thoughts and their emotions. But remember, emotions are subtle mental images which when given enough time and energy become thoughts, which most people interpret as feelings, and then these thoughts can plague the mind and the body. The heart, the seat of all emotion, is made only to realize and love God. It is not meant for anything else. The love that one feels for people, things, images, worldly objects does not arise from the heart but is a combination of the mind, the impressions gathered from the womb stage and one's karmic bond with that person or place or experience.

'Say, for example, you see somebody and you fall in love with that person. The mind is telling you to avoid, but there is something more powerful which compels you to move towards the person and pursue the relationship. Now what is that compelling factor? It may be physical attraction, or it could be that the person reminds you of somebody you have loved before, or has some karmic bond with you from the past which requires balancing and thus there is the pull towards each other or various other reasons. Remember, the heart is meant only to realize God and when you move within the heart chakra all that you will truly realize is Oneness. Most often, relationships are karmic. Why do you love your children so much even though they keep hurting you? Why out of the many children you have a special place in your heart for one of them? How can you allow somebody to walk all over you and nobody else? This has got nothing to do with the heart but more to do with the karmic bond of give and take.

'Then the mind or intellect decides whether you are going to give yourself a taste of heaven or you are to swim in the quicksand of hell. Not the heart, but the mind. That is why it is imperative that you are the master of your mind or intellect. Let us say a thought or emotion comes to you. You have the power of nurturing that thought or emotion. You have the power of dismissing that thought or emotion. You have the thought of being obsessed with that thought or emotion. You have the power of completely ignoring that thought or emotion. You have the power of being completely destroyed by that thought or emotion. Emotion is a thought which may or may not have reason. So your want to possess a woman or a man, it does not come from the heart but more from the seat of passion and power, which means from the three root chakras.

'So when a thought arises, you have the power to delete the thought or emotion impulse. Or you have the power to store it and then you may or may not use it later, but it is stored in your memory card or, as people say, in the subconscious mind. Then you have the power to give the thought the energy and form a spark; by giving energy or attention, you make the spark a fire, then turn the fire into a raging fire and then the raging fire into an inferno, which in all probability shall burn you to smithereens or ashes or take you on the wings of the angels to soar heights, even make you reach Oneness.

'So the thought which arises as an electrical impulse can be immediately deleted, can be stored, can be nurtured, can be made into an obsession, and if the thought given power to is not holistic in nature, which means it is not for the overall well-being of you, your Higher Self and those around you, then disaster takes place, and if the thought given attention is for the well-being of your spiritual self or the well-being of those around you then goodness and calmness prevails.

'So when a thought comes about, you should be in the power of rejecting it, storing it, using it for your well-being and the well-being of those around you. But nowadays most people have no control over thoughts. They are slaves to their thoughts. Thoughts of lust, love, anger, greed, sloth, power, material possession, power over others, and the individual is a slave. The individual does not have any power over those thoughts. Twenty thoughts running in and out like bastards, screaming and shouting, and the individual is like a chutiya with no control or power to thrash them out and live in peace with who s(h)e wants as guest or co-occupant.

'So when you are in control of your mind then you are in control of your life, your emotions, your sanity and your harmony. But when your thoughts rule you, you are like a slave in your own house.'

'You love to talk, na Baba? I have not understood one word You've spoken. How does one get a grip over one's thoughts?'

'First and foremost, when a thought comes to you, you have the power to delete, store, encourage. If the thought is not for one's overall well-being, ideally you should delete it and if you cannot then make sure you neither encourage it or fight it. If you encourage the thought or fight the thought, you are giving it energy or power or strength. Thus, the best thing to do is try one's level best to neither encourage the thought or fight the thought. Shift your attention to the present moment, or chant or distract yourself with something else. If there is something that needs your attention, give it, but always set a time limit. Let us say a thought is bothering you, and you cannot ignore it or shift your mind to the present moment, then the next best thing is to sit with the thought for a quantified period of time, say, ten minutes, half an hour, an hour, and after that time frame go back to your present moment. Thus what you have done is that you have given permission to your mind to entertain the thought, but also made it clear that you are in charge and you will decide when to encourage and when to delete and when to store each thought or emotional impulse that comes within your orbit. You have to make it clear to your mind, heart, body, that you are in charge. If you do not then there is chaos.

'Initially you might have innumerable thoughts. Slowly, slowly, slowly, keep getting into the moment, keep chanting, keep coming back to yourself, and slowly you will be once again the master of your own self. The mind is the greatest servant and the worst master. Know this for sure. *Forget the devil, your mind is enough to make you live in hell for all of eternity*. Remember, even after you leave your body, the mind accompanies you and the thoughts that plagued you in the body will continue to plague you even when you are in the spirit world and most earthbound spirits are those who were ruled by their thoughts and mind. Thus, make sure that slowly but surely you get in control of your mind. Remember, beta, either you can give your best to live and leave the rest to your Master and make peace with the situation, or you can rot in the abyss of your private hell, which is the mind not in control over you but controlling you with thoughts that you are now powerless to control. So you can be in control or be controlled. It is up to each individual.

'Like I have said often and all the Sufis, including Abdul, have recorded this, before you proceed on the path of Allah, you must discipline the mind. Strengthen the mind and as there is continuous warfare, strengthen the defences. It is simple, Rabda, if there is continuous war, the army must be most alert. If the army is not alert, one has lost the war already. If the army does not move how can the war of righteousness be fought? And most important, the heart has no army, the wazir has the army. So if you want to live peacefully, the intellect should be alert and in your command. The heart as I have said before is for the realization of God and a human being's only priority should be to realize God. To attain the vision of God is every true being's only priority and for the vision of God, Divine Sight is a must and Divine Sight can only come to one whose intellect is under his or her control and moving towards the vision of God. Thus it is imperative to have your mind under your control and for that one needs to live in the moment, practise naam samaran, or constant chanting of God's name and know that it is with a calm, controlled mind that the doors of heaven will open. And if the heart is in chaos, how can the heart spend its each throb chanting the Name?'

The need to go within, be calm, should be a priority. It should be as important as breathing.

'Baba, Your favourite words were "Faith and Patience", shraddha aur saburi . . .'

'No, bachcha, my favourite words were "Allah Malik, sab ka Malik ek hain aur Allah bhala karega . . ."'

'Okay, but You were big on telling everybody to have faith and patience. Why?'

'Bachcha, what nobody has truly understood is the significance of these two simple words, faith and patience. When can you have faith and patience? If an individual keeps chanting "faith and patience" without realizing what is required to walk the path of faith and patience, then both these words are meaningless. The foundation of living a life with faith and patience is complete trust in God and all that which happens does so without the permission of the Lord and Master, and if something were to happen with the permission of the Lord and Master, then whatever is taking place has the permission of the Lord and Master. Whatever happens takes place, one undergoes it, one has His or Her blessings and permission, thus all is well.

'What is required for faith and patience is more important than all the spiritual scriptures ever written or spoken.

Faith and patience are the foundation and pillars of all that which is spiritual and godly. Now let us take each word and understand all that which is required to follow the true meaning and live the true essence of each word.

'Take the first word, "faith". What does faith mean? Faith means having complete trust that whatever has been ordained is for your best well-being and larger good, no matter how difficult, humiliating, horrific that experience and phase or even life may be. When each individual understands that God is just and that God is impartial and that God is all-loving and all-merciful and that God is all-knowing, then the individual begins to understand that nothing can take place which is not for the overall best for him or her. You must understand that what each one goes through is because of his or her own karma, which is moulded by one's actions and thoughts and words. We all have to go through the ramifications of our free will used in some lifetime. Free will used in a lifetime comes to either haunt or crush us or embrace and bless us in some future time or lifetime. When we know that we are going through the ramifications of our karma and we know for sure that God is all-merciful and just and loving, so S(H)e would never hurt and harm any living being, and that S(H)e would want each child to be happy, joyful, free, liberated from all pain and agony and sadness. Take the love and compassion of every mother and father, who has ever been, is and will be, put all that love and compassion together—it would not be the tip of an iceberg when compared to the love and compassion of our Maker. Understand this. Know this. Believe this. This is the eternal truth, that S(H)e loves us so much that all that S(H)e wants is that each one realizes Oneness and experiences the Eternal Glory, Power and Radiance. Imagine, all God wants is that every individual recognize his or her own Godhood and not worship God but embrace God and eventually become God.

'So when you understand that all that we go through is because of free will used at some time which has gone wrong and we are only experiencing the ramifications of our thoughts, words, actions, and that when we suffer, our God and Master suffer the angst along with us, you will comprehend God's love for you and love for each individual and being.

'So faith comes about when you know that no matter how bad the situation is, your Master and God is with you, walking the path, holding your hand, wiping your tears, applying balm on your broken heart, infusing your being with love and strength and fortitude to go through the experience with calmness, courage, grace and dignity, then each one understands what faith stands for. Faith does not mean the problem will be resolved. Faith means you are not alone and God knows best and your God, Master and guides and angels are with you and that you are not alone. *Faith does not mean miracles. Faith itself is the miracle, as faith means you will go through whatever is in store for you gracefully and that, my child, is the greatest miracle.* A miracle is not about getting a watch out of thin air and curing illness and bringing the dead back to life, these things are not miracles. These things are side shows. *The real miracle is to bring an individual from darkness into the Light. The real miracle is converting harshness into tenderness.* The real miracle is going through agony with a smile and still spreading happiness around. The real miracle is being cheated and still blessing the one who has cheated you. The real miracle is having no water but still making sure others do not go thirsty. Bachcha, these are real miracles. Wiping another's tears when your heart is bleeding is the true miracle. So when you have faith, you know that we are the gods of our destiny and we shall reap what we have sowed, but God never judges and never condemns and that S(H)e will always be with us even when the whole world has turned its back on us. So a man or woman who understands all this will understand what faith is. Faith is not "God, sort this or that out for me" but "God, I know you are with me and You and I will go through this experience and, God, bless me to go through this experience such that I make You happy and proud of me." That is faith, bachcha. So when I tell you to have faith, I am not telling you convenient faith but all-encompassing faith. And that faith will come from love.

'You know, Rabda, what is my greatest sorrow? My greatest regret is the number of my children, devotees, disciples who chant my name out of love, selfless love, without expecting anything in return but love. How many truly love me, my son? How many want nothing from me, but just love? How many seek only my love and not even liberation or escaping the clutches of illusions or the laws of cause and effect? How many love God or Goddess or me or the Masters for the sake of only love, my bachcha? Is there not something that each child expects and wants out of the One? How many came to meet me for love? How many, Rabda? How many wanted what I wanted to give them? How many walked away from the open vault of spirituality and Godhood and settled for a job, a spouse, a child, health, money, power? Who wanted what this fakir wanted to give them? No, bachcha, when you approach God or Master with a business proposition, then God and Master walk towards you with what you seek. Seek and you shall receive. But when you truly love, true faith will come about and that is why I kept telling everybody, Faith, Faith, Faith, but they grasped the word faith as a business deal. Have faith so your Master will have no other option but to comply and not as have faith as your Master knows what is best for you. But those who understood the word for what it truly stood and stands for, their lives changed. Faith is, as I have told you, the pillar of all spiritual growth. That is why the path of bhakti is considered the fastest and easiest way to reach the One, as bhakti is based on love but true love, love for the sake of love. No other reason but love. When you have love, faith follows and with that, the path clears up and you walk the path that leads to the home of Oneness. Thus, I said it on and on and on, Faith.

'Then comes patience. Saburi. This word itself is a path to salvation. Patience does not mean waiting for something, it means having the faith that God knows when the time is right for you. The Lord knows when you should get what you desire and whether you should get what you desire and the best time when you should get what you desire. The word patience means to know that the Lord knows what is best for you and thus knows when is the best time for you. Once again, when you love the One, have faith that S(H)e knows what is best for you, then automatically, you not only leave the timing of deliverance, but also whether you are justified and entitled to the deliverance. So, you are not expecting anything, any time, you have left everything at all times. Do you understand, you disgruntled, constipated mule?'

'Eh. I mean, I am like a good child listening to You go on and on and on and then You call me these enlightening words, but I have faith and patience in You, thus I shall continue to listen. Go on, Mr Baba.'

'Arrey, shaitan, devil you are, so patience is being awake at one in the morning, knowing that the Lord knows when is the best time for either you to fall asleep or for the sun to rise and that the good Lord knows why it should rise in the east and that if the sun were not to be seen in the east but in the west, that too must be for a good reason, and whether the sun rises at six or four in the afternoon, even that the good Lord knows best. Patience is not standing by the window, fretting and fuming and pacing and grunting till the sun rises. That is not patience. That is stupidity and lack of faith. Thus, instead making a nuisance of oneself all through the night, the wise person would try to sleep and if sleep still evades, the person would gently and calmly pass the night, in prayer, reading, hearing music, working, watching a good movie or doing anything but not ranting, and abusing and worrying. That is patience. Calm acceptance of what is happening and knowing when the experience has to end or what time it has to end or come to the fore, the good Lord knows best. Thus patience comes about with the right faith and when you have the right kind of uncomplicated, unbusinesslike faith, then the right kind of patience comes about and once you have the pristine, childlike forms of faith and patience, then, trust me, spiritual growth, peace, calmness, centredness are assured.

'Thus, for me, for the child who has to live a life in the world, with worldly responsibilities, true faith and patience is equivalent to the reading of all scriptures and holy books and meditation and chanting and everything. True faith and patience is living God by truly loving God, Goddess and Master. This is the eternal truth and thus I would tell one and all, faith and patience, but I wonder how many truly understood what true faith and patience in all their spiritual power meant?'

Rabda saw Baba smile. In that smile Rabda realized true faith and patience. The faith that mankind would one day walk the path to Divine Light. The patience that no matter how messed up we all are, one day, we will drop all the baggage that ties us down and soar heaven-bound.

Rabda sighed. This dream was something. If he was dreaming, life would become a heavier cross to bear when he woke up. And if he was dead, then he wanted neither salvation, liberation, joy, nothing, all he wanted was to be with Baba in this cave for all of eternity and just be.

'Rabda, I love you.'

Rabda walked up to Baba and put his head near Baba's feet and began to weep as he had never done before.

In the hospital room, the old nurse saw tears flowing down the cheeks of her famous patient. She looked at him and was certain she had never seen him look so peaceful. She saw the medical parameters. The doctors were convinced their patient had played his last song and that it was only a matter of time before the curtains would draw down and though she had never met the man when he was conscious, though she had never heard his music, though she had never really experienced the essence of the man, she hoped that the man would open his eyes once and smile that sad, loopy smile of his, but she from over thirty-five years of medical service was aware that only a miracle would bring the man back into the world of the living, as now for some reason he was truly comfortable in the world of the beyond.

The moment you drop the illusion that you are the body, you begin to give power to your very soul to soar to the Source.

They were back in Shirdi. Caiz was very keen on seeing Baba's life after the three-day samadhi. He had been told by Baba often that after 1886 and especially from 1909 things changed drastically in the lives of those who lived in Shirdi. From a mad fakir known to those living in Shirdi and surrounding villages, Baba Sai slowly became a known name throughout the country. And when Caiz saw what was going on in Shirdi in those last twelve to fifteen years before Baba left His body, he was astounded. Innumerable people arrived in Shirdi. Gone were those quiet days. Now it was like a mela or a perpetual carnival and, yes, from a Sufi or a fakir, now Baba began to be treated like a God or a deity, worshipped by Hindus, Zoroastrians, Christians and, yes, a number of Muslims, mainly fakirs and wandering seekers and those who wanted help for the Mecca pilgrimage or financial help to keep body and soul together. Caiz saw it all and was truly flabbergasted.

It was like a movie and he saw various facets of Baba Sai, sometimes Sai joking with His devotees who were His friends too. Sai dancing in the guest or travel house, where numerous Sufis would come to meet Him, was a thing of the past. After His first samadhi, for some reason, Baba Sai had stopped dancing and singing songs in various languages, especially Persian and Arabic. But now more and more of Baba Sai showing His various Divine Forms, especially that of Lord Dattatreya and Lord Vithal and other avatars, had commenced. Slowly, Shirdi no longer was a small town, but an epicentre of spiritual activity, thanks to a fakir in torn clothes who performed miracles with such alarming regularity that anything and everything was possible.

Sai raging and thrashing the living daylights out of people and abusing them in such a prolific manner that it would give drunkard sailors a complex. Baba Sai loving His devotees with such motherly tenderness that Caiz would begin to weep. Baba Sai taking on the illness of His children and suffering such horrific physical agony that only a Perfect Master can embrace it happily. Baba Sai gardening. Baba Sai asking for money from what seemed like one and all, but in reality asking from only those the Fakir pointed to Him and refusing money from many who He was not directed towards. Baba Sai earning more than the Governor of India, but every night going to sleep with a few paisas, just enough to buy oil and tobacco.

Baba Sai as a Hindu sage. Baba Sai as a Sufi and Friend of God. Baba Sai at times a traditional Muslim and then Baba Sai behaving in a manner that nobody would ever believe He could be a follower of Islam. He was such an enigma and the best part of it all was that He loved confusing people about His birth and religion. He loved playing with those interested not in His Godhood and spirituality but the triviality of which religion He was born to or followed. He loved confusing people about His past. Sometimes He would hint that He was a Hindu. Sometimes, a Muslim. Sometimes His Guru was Roshan Shah, who was obviously a Muslim and to many He would say Venkusa, who was a Hindu. Both sound the same, Roshan Shah and Venkusa. He would have Allah Malik on His lips, recite the Sureh Fatia and then go about doing everything not appreciated by Muslims, like allowing devotees of other faiths to perform and sing the aarti, treating Him clearly as their presiding Deity, God and Master and then of course His love for Lord Hanuman was known far and wide. Dare anybody say a word against Lord Hanuman and then Baba would swear and abuse. So He was an enigma. Most of the world considered Him to be either a Sufi or a mad fakir. The irony was that all Sufis considered Him to be a friend of God and all sages who met Him or spoke of Him considered Him to be One with God. But the common man never gave up either trying to fix a religion with His name or malign Him by calling Him various names.

But Caiz realized that Baba cared a flying fuck for everything. He just did not care what people thought of Him or spoke about Him. He was oblivious to praise and criticism. He was so detached that one would never be sure if Baba was truly spiritual or just a mad man. He would often talk to Himself, abuse nobody in particular, sing, dance, laugh, and people would wonder who was He addressing and Caiz realized that Baba was never alone. He was always with Light Workers and other Spiritual Masters who came to seek His company or guidance and spirits who wanted a release or agents of God who took instructions of Baba and went about doing Baba's work all over the world and other spirit dimensions.

Baba Sai was always chanting 'Allah Malik', God is the Master, and would keep telling one and all, 'Sab ka Malik ek hain', which meant 'Everybody's God is one', but nobody really understood what He was trying to tell them, that God came before and beyond religion.

The numerous daily miracles that Caiz saw Baba perform day after day, miracles that became so commonplace, included making the rain stop by just looking up at the sky and saying, 'Hold on now, my children, have to catch the train' and the rain halting; telling a falling roof, 'Sabar, abhi nahi', meaning 'Have patience, not now'; Baba consuming His lunch along with His innermost disciples and then walking out and looking back and the roof caving down; burning oil lamps without the oil but by consuming water and then removing the water into the mud vessels that were meant to contain the oil for the lamps; knowing the past, present and future, so effortlessly, of all those who came to Him—without going into any trance or taking time off or anything, casually, like talking about weather, He would reveal that He knew all; being able to read the minds of all those who were near Him or knowing the words spoken by those years ago; you could hide nothing from Him, nothing; saving a child who was about to fall into fire far away by shoving His hand into Dwarka Mai's Holy Fire, and burning His hand badly and then days later thankful parents bursting into tears with gratitude for His saving their child. Baba was different.

Caiz realized that He was so cool, so unassuming, so

different and yet so the One. Yes, He would go into fits of fury and thrash one and all, and Caiz could not help bursting in laughter seeing strong-built men diving for shelter when Baba had His outbursts. Miracles were thus commonplace and they became so routine that eventually nobody batted an eyelid but for some reason Caiz realized that these miracles also got people in truckloads, not for the love of Baba, but for material gain. Nothing is wrong with that, only a person who cannot put food on the table for his or her starving children understands the importance of money, but Caiz was certain that even Baba realized that people had lost the plot. For every ten thousand who came to Baba, maybe a hundred or less came to Baba for spiritual well-being and out of those hundred, maybe one came because the person truly loved Baba.

But beyond the miracles and wisdom and love and divinity and everything, one thing that was constant with Baba was His strange dislike for change of routine and basically dislike or resistance towards change of any kind. Thus Baba had a routine and Caiz never failed to get amazed by this routine and nothing short of a miracle could bring about a change in His routine.

So Baba would rise much before dawn, that is, if He actually slept. According to Avatar Meher Baba, Perfect Masters never in reality slept. Even if They appeared to be snoring in reality They reposed between the sixth and seventh plane, still aware, very much helping those who called out to Them. But Baba rarely slept. Sometimes He would take forty winks, while all sang devotional songs and did the aarti, He appeared to take a snooze and then He would know exactly all that which transpired when He was apparently snoring His gorgeous and loving head off. So Baba was always awake long before dawn and He would always be muttering to Himself, always in some eternal chant. He would keep chanting, eyes shut, near Dhuni Mai, back to the pillar, sometimes touching the pillar, and very often His back would not even take the support of the pillar.

Baba was a Sufi and one of the tenants of Sufism, Caiz realized, was to make life a bloody living hell for the one walking the path, by his avoiding all comforts; all recourse to making life easy was to be clearly avoided. Embrace poverty, sleep less, eat less, and do all this happily, with gratitude.

Thus, before dawn itself Baba would sit near the Holy Fire and chant and nobody was allowed close to Him, sometimes not within a fifty-foot distance of Him. After meditation He would chant words like 'Allah Malik hain', 'Yaade Haq', 'Allah wali hain', and Caiz noticed that Baba would perform some mudras, which were yogic positioning of fingers, touching various parts of the palms. Namaste itself is a yogic mudra. Abdul was always around from the time Baba would wake up and though Abdul was married and had a family, his service to Baba continued and the best part of it all was that Baba never gave Abdul any monetary compensation, though Baba was really big and firm on paying each person much more than the worth of service they provided; with Abdul, Baba gave him no money, but the assurance that Abdul would cross the seven dimensions and no longer be part of the karmic cycle. The love Abdul had for Baba was understandable but the respect he professed for Baba, in spite of years of being together, was commendable—not once did Abdul take Baba for granted or talk to Him in any other way but with complete respect.

There was another young man called Madhav Fasle who accompanied Abdul and they went about cleaning and taking care of Dwarka Mai. Abdul all his life cleaned Dwarka Mai and the lanes which Baba walked.

Then came Bhagoji Shinde, who suffered from leprosy— and with Baba's grace, it did not progress and was contained; for the last eight years before Baba took samadhi, Bhagoji would come to Dwarka Mai and massage Baba's burnt hand. The same hand Baba had put into Dhuni Mai to save the child from being charred to death miles away.

So Bhagoji would apply some clarified butter and then bandage Baba's hand and though Baba's hand had healed years before, Bhagoji would go through the process each morning and Baba Sai would allow Bhagoji to do whatever he wanted. The bandage would be opened, then cleansed, then little ghee would be applied, a soft massage given, then a new or old bandage put again. This happened every day from 1910 to 1918.

'I allowed Bhagaya to do so for various reasons. First and foremost this was his love for me. He loved me so selflessly and he had been with me for lifetimes so we had our bond. Secondly, by him serving me, Bhagaya's main purpose to accelerate the process of karmic cleansing, for which he had taken on the form of a leper, was being achieved. Remember, most often, those who take on leprosy in a particular lifetime are not sinners of the worst lot as assumed by many, but in fact love God and the One so much that they cannot bear the distance and cannot wait for lifetimes to merge, so in one lifetime they plan their karmic cleansing, which most people spread through many lifetimes. Thus for all of us, Swami Samarth, my Meher, myself, lepers are beautiful butterflies longing for the final metamorphosis. The third reason was that all those who needed healing were being healed by Bhagaya's service to me. Do you understand, you demented worm?'

'I do not remember even asking You a question. I am following the Sufi modus operandi: speak little and go beyond an grumpy old Master's yak yak.'

So then after the massage, Bhagoji would go and prepare Baba's chillum. Baba would take a few puffs and hand it to Bhagoji who would take in a few drags and hand it back to Baba. After this spiritual passing-the-smoking-parcel, Bhagoji would go about his work of waiting on Baba.

By now there were innumerable devotees waiting for Baba and it would be around seven or seven thirty when the Royal Darbar would be kind of open for the King to meet His devotees. There would be talk about everything under the sun during this meeting and often Baba would predict something or the other, or talk about what He did the previous night, the astral travel, the paranormal experiences, which eventually would be confirmed either via a letter, a message of thanks or a personal visit to Baba.

Baba never brushed His teeth. He would gargle and that was that. He never took a bath every day. Once in a while there was a divine fragrance that came from His body. Baba would often say that there are various ways to have a bath. There was the sun or surya bath where you invited the sun to cleanse you. Then there was the wind bath. Then there was a bath one took by manipulating your breath. And then you had the normal water bath. For most sages, the bath with water cleansed you the least.

These yogis, I tell you! contemplated Caiz—the buggers will go all out and do things differently.

Baba would but wash His face, hands and feet in the most tender manner and the water was then used by those suffering from leprosy and so many got healed or their conditions improved dramatically by the water that had cleansed Baba's body. A number of those suffering from various long-term illnesses would drink this water and even those suffering from mental disorders recovered.

Earlier Baba would bathe in Lendi Garden but later on He began to have a bath once a week, sometimes once in a few weeks, but in Dwarka Mai itself. Abdul or some attendant would bring two vessels, copper vessels, with boiling hot water and another two with cold water. Baba would mix the water and then have a bath, very slowly, very calmly, sometimes taking over an hour and a half to bathe. He would wear a langot, or a native underwear, while He bathed, and then He would stand in front of Dhuni Mai, the Holy Fire, while His attendants dried His body. He would remove His underwear but first he'd wrap a green cloth or towel around His waist and then He would stand by the Fire and also His robe was put in front of the Fire to dry and then He would wear the same one as usual.

As mentioned, this water was then used or consumed by a number of those suffering from various physical, emotional and mental ailments, all recovering, depending upon their faith but, most importantly, depending upon their love for Baba.

Caiz realized that with or without a bath His Baba was always neat and clean though His kafni and bandana were in various degrees of wear and tear. His kafni was made of coarse cloth and stitched wherever torn and Baba Himself would stitch it and often the robe looked more stitched and with patches all over, but this is how Sufis wore their robes. It was the sign of embracing poverty with pride.

He would rarely give His kafni to anybody but put it into the Holy Fire and when He wore a new kafni He would make sure He would donate new kafnis to various Sufis and sages present with Him at that time. But Caiz realized to get his Old Man to discard the kafni was a task. Time and again His devotees would tell Baba to wear a new one or allow them to present Him one but He would smile and say no. But when His kafni really got old and torn, Tatya would come close to Baba and then as though asking Him something, he would put his finger in the torn patch of a kafni and then tug at it, creating a bigger hole, and then tell Baba that this kafni was too torn to be worn and Baba would rant and rave and abuse and then exhale and smile. So Baba, now having no choice, would call for the village cloth-dealer Kashinath Shimpri and He would tell him, 'Kashya, get me a new kafni.'

So Kashinath would hasten and bring Baba His new kafni and along with Baba's new kafni he would get more kafnis, as he was aware of Baba's habit of gifting other sages and Sufis with new kafnis and Baba would say a prayer, remove the old kafni, throw the old one into the Holy Fire, chanting prayers, and then wear the new one. He would then pay Kashinath far more than the worth of the kafnis.

On and off Baba would get His head shaved and moustache trimmed by Bala the barber and pay him enough for good man Bala to retire for the day.

Then depending on where Baba slept that night, the early morning aarti would take place and all this would be over by eight, as all were aware that by eight Baba went out for His morning round of begging from five houses. A very important point that Caiz saw was that the Holy Ash would be given to all devotees by Bhagoji, the one inflicted with leprosy.

'Rabda, it is important that Bhagya distributed the Udhi. If Baba Sai finds a man good enough to massage His arm for so many years and then smoke from the same chillum that the man smokes from, then why should that man be differentiated when giving Holy Ash from our Dhuni Mai? Those who have faith will take it as my prasad. Those who do not have faith or flinch or hesitate or doubt, even if they take the Udhi, but will not benefit from the Ash. It is all about love, Rabda. When you love me then my vomit will heal, just as my vomited onion gave a devotee spiritual powers and the power of whatever he spoke coming true. Thus it is all about love, bachcha.'

Baba never ate in anybody's home and also He never cooked for Himself and also He never kept food for the next meal. He had left all to the One, the same One who provides food for birds and all creatures would provide food to this humble fakir was His logic.

Yes there were times before 1910, when Baba used to cook for His devotees. He would shop for all the ingredients, haggle, win the haggle, then pay the vendor far more than what the person had initially demanded, wash everything, make the spices, then in big handis or pots would cook food. One pot would be for those who ate non-vegetarian food and the other for those who ate only vegetarian food. When the huge pot would be on boil, Baba would roll up His sleeve and put His hand in the boiling broth and stir the broth with His bare hand. But after 1910, there used to be so many devotees bringing food as prasad that Baba stopped cooking.

He would keep a cloth hanging on His shoulder and hold the other end of the cloth. All dry food, rice, baked bread or roti and sweetmeats were put into this cloth. He would carry a tin and all liquid, be it curd, cooked pulses, buttermilk, whatever, went into the pot.

Baba would come out of Dwarka Mai, stand in front of Lord Hanuman's temple, sometimes for over twenty minutes, sometimes He would chant and sometimes He would make hand gestures and draw symbols and then look at the Chavadi.

He then would beg at the five houses in an order. First He would go to go to Sakharam Shelke's house and call out to Sakharam's wife, 'Itlayi bai, roti lao', meaning 'Sister Itlayi, give me a roti', then in front of Waman Gondkar's house and then to Appaji Patil's house where He would call out 'bhakri de' meaning 'give me roti', then He would go to Bayaja Ma and after she passed away, to her son, Tatya's house and call out, 'Bayaja Ma, jevan de, roti lao' meaning 'Mother Bayaja, give me food, get the roti', and then conclude His journey at Nanduram Marwadi's house, where Baba Sai, the king of the Universe, would call out, either to Nanduram, 'Nanduram bhakri de' or to his wife, Radha, 'Bopidi bai mithai de'.

Bopidi means to stutter, and our Baba would call Radhabai bopidi with love and she would leave all her work, make a proper sweetmeat for Baba and then Baba would put a small morsel of it in His mouth and then distribute it to all those who were with Him. Earlier Baba would go alone but once His fame grew, there was no chance, Caiz realized, that the poor Man could be alone anywhere, but in Dwarka Mai and Lendi Garden. Baba would love to nickname one and all and He said it with so much love that those being nicknamed would feel blessed.

Also Baba being Baba, He would go to the same houses, in the same order, and eventually bless them all by saying, 'Abaad-e-abaad, Allah bhala karega', meaning, 'Allah will do good and keep you and your lot prosperous'. There were also times when Baba would go as many as eight times to each house in a day. This is where His routine did not come about.

Caiz realized that there was a spiritual reason for Baba going to the five houses. He remembered reading that the five houses stand for Five Perfect Masters, as explained by Avatar Meher Baba and there was a spiritual significance and going there, sometimes many times, had a universal significance.

Baba Sai would then halt at a particular place and feed dogs and crows and if there was any other animal and then return to Dwarka Mai, where He would offer either rice or roti to the sacred Dhuni Mai and then mix all the food in a open mud vessel or pot-like structure which He called kundi. Often animals and birds would eat from this pot and then sometimes beggars would come and take some and cleaners and sweepers would take some and Baba would smile and go about His chanting and sitting in front of Dhuni Mai and then He would put a few morsels in His mouth and then the food was distributed as prasad or Holy Offerings.

Sometimes Baba would send one of His devotees to beg at the five houses, and once He made a devotee who was dear to Him, G.G. Narke, go and beg for food, all in a three-piece suit and the devotee did so happily and with all humility and it pleased Baba so much that on and off for four months, when Baba was unwell, Narke would plead to be sent to beg and Baba would oblige, of course sometimes with loud abuses.

Baba did not care for food or the taste of the food. He begged for food till virtually the last week of His physical life, when in the last few days He could barely walk, but still managed to do so for the sake of His devotees. Often when unwell, He would make His devotees support Him and He would go and beg at the five houses. Obviously there was a huge spiritual significance to this five-house pilgrimage.

Also Baba suffered immensely all His life from asthma, constipation and intestinal issues. He never complained but often the pain and discomfort would be so gripping that those near Him would begin to cry and He would then comfort them by saying that His Fakir knew best so keep calm and He would recover. Once His dear disciple, Raghuvir Purandare, began to weep seeing Baba's state and Baba told him, 'Oh Raghu, why are you crying, nothing has happened to Me. Do not worry. It will be better shortly.' Often the pain and discomfort was extreme but He would go about His prayers

and chanting and begging and meeting and blessing all those
who came to Him, and Caiz began to weep too.

For constipation He would make some broth with leaves
of sonamukhi and other herbs and drink it and maybe out
of His sense of humour would make others drink it along
with Him. For conjunctivitis, He would make paste of black
pepper and apply the paste into His eyes.

'I guess You never heard of eye drops, hunh, my Baba?'

'Very funny. Just watch and be amazed.'

'Ya, You are all humility personified.'

Around eight thirty or nine, Baba would then proceed
towards Lendi Garden. Earlier, He would go physically
alone, but always accompanied by Rabda and other spirit
bodies but as Baba's name and fame grew, the entire journey
to Lendi Garden became like a procession.

He would step out of Dwarka Mai and then face Lord
Hanuman's temple. He would spend time looking at Lord
Hanuman and very often gesticulate certain signs which
nobody really could fathom. There were times He would
stand for as long as twenty-odd minutes looking at Lord
Hanuman—once He had told a devotee, 'You want to know
who my parents are, there, see Him, Lord Hanuman', thus
it was very obvious that Baba was very attached to Lord
Hanuman. The fact that He had told Shama that both He and
Shama were with Lord Rama during the time the bridge was
constructed to Lanka should signify a lot of His attachment
or association with Lord Rama and Lord Hanuman.

Then He would halt at Gurusthan, a place where His
Guru's samadhi under the neem tree reposed. When Baba
Sai had first come to Shirdi, even before entering Shirdi with

Chand Patil, He was barely a sixteen-year-old lad. He used to sit and meditate for long hours, sometimes through the day and night, under the neem tree, and when the villagers had asked the village psychic, who would channel Lord Khandoba to the identity of the young lad, Lord Khandoba through the village psychic had come through and had directed the villagers to the neem tree under which there was a pathway that led to a samadhi, which was lit by eternal oil lamps. Though Baba had told one and all that the samadhi was of His Guru, many were certain that either the samadhi was of Baba's Guru, but not from this lifetime, or the samadhi itself was of Baba from another lifetime. Anyway, Baba would stand near the Gurusthan and as though communicating with somebody, who Caiz realized were Eternal Masters in spirit form, then Baba would begin His journey to Lendi Garden.

The devotees who had come in droves from Bombay and other towns and cities would all stand in line and those staying at the newly constructed guest houses, Wadas, too would come out on the streets, and Baba like royalty would walk through the columns of people, on either side of the street, greeting and blessing and halting to talk to a few of them, most of the time asking each one by name of their well-being. He knew all and He knew the past, present and future of all. Bhagoji would hold a ceremonial umbrella over Baba's head, Nana would be on one side of Baba and Botty on the other, while Baba, a king in torn clothes, would walk slowly, His body now slowly giving in but His smile and His eyes, what powerful eyes He had, radiant as ever, the sun paling in front of Baba Sai's splendour! An emperor who lived by begging for His food. Royalty who had both the spirit world and the physical at His feet.

Baba would only wear footwear when He went to Lendi Garden and, even then, often would go barefoot. Baba would then cross Lord Vithal's temple, then cross the Kanifnath temple and then move towards the garden.

Only Abdul was allowed to enter the garden with Baba. Caiz noticed a lamp burning, which during the time Baba was in the body, was ever-burning. The lamp was put into a small depression, nearly two feet in the ground, and covered with a zinc sheet, and then around the depression and lamp, around twenty-odd curtains were draped, forming a tent around the lamp, and Abdul would stay here and look after the eternal lamp. As soon as Baba entered the garden, Abdul would fill two vessels of water and place them near Baba. He would then go about cleaning the place while Baba sat, His back to the lamp, and would chant something or the other and sprinkle the water in all directions. Even Abdul was not allowed near Baba when He sprinkled the water in all directions and then would move in one direction, stand and stare in that direction and then return and again move into another direction and do the same. Obviously, it was a spiritual practice which meant far more than just sprinkling water.

After an hour or so Baba would make His journey back to Dwarka Mai, following the same route He had previously taken to Lendi Garden.

From ten to eleven thirty, Baba would sit in Dwarka Mai, and devotees would come and meet Him, be guided by Him, be blessed and nurtured by Him, and of course a few would be abused and thrashed by Him too. When angry, Baba became like a lion, age and health notwithstanding, and tough men would flee rather than come in between Him and His rage. But He would get calm as quickly as He would heat up like a rocket.

Musicians, magicians, drama people, Sufi singers, all would come and perform and Baba would bless them and send them off with gifts, money and food. Sometimes Baba would once again go for a round to beg for food. The only thing that was not in routine was the number of times He begged for food at the five homes.

Later on when there were so many devotees, Baba would keep a little food in the mud vessel and also mix a little food He had begged with all the other food brought by devotees and that food was distributed as prasad or holy offering. Baba rarely ate food and when food was offered. He would touch the food and that food was distributed to one and all, the devotees, the Sufis, the sages, the beggars, the artists, all were fed. Baba loved to feed one and all. During the season of mangoes, He would get the mangoes cut, take a piece or two, and then distribute the fruit and often He would buy mangoes and get them distributed to all.

Baba was very fond of children and He would keep sweetmeats for the kids and make sure the children got sweetmeats and fruits first. Very often, if the kids were off to school or not present Baba would keep the sweetmeats and certain delicacies for the children and then He would personally give each one and joke with them and become a child with them.

With elders Baba did not speak much, unless He was in

one of His moods. He would recount what experiences He had in the night, the spiritual, paranormal journeys He had undertaken, and in a few hours or a day or two, all that Baba had spoken, which sounded like one of those fantastic stories, would be proved as reality and as the truth.

Baba earlier would speak plainly and to the point, but as people gathered more and more around Him, Baba began to speak in parables and through stories. Mainly because He had to get His point across to a person, or a family, without everybody knowing for whom the story or parable was recounted. As He could not often speak to each and every devotee gathered personally. The art of speaking in parables began from the year 1910 and that is why many books assume Baba only spoke in parables, which is untrue. He earlier spoke to the point and frankly and without any shadow boxing but desperate times need desperate measures, realized Caiz.

At eleven thirty, the bells in Dwarka Mai would be rung which meant it was time for aarti or the holy songs to be sung. This routine was started around 1903 and all would gather and with Baba as the presiding deity, the aarti would begin. Baba had earlier resisted this ritual but seeing the love and devotion of His devotees had given in and though the rigid Muslims had objected, saying for a Sufi this was blasphemy, Baba had relented to having the aarti, saying that for the love of His devotees, all is permissible. In the aarti thus all communities would gather and it was a sight to see.

Baba seated as the presiding God of Dwarka Mai, and His devotees praying to Him. His eyes would glow. He would make signs, He would smile, He would throw fierce glances often, and devotees would smile, cry and be mesmerized by their loving God, the fakir of fakirs, the One and Only, Baba Sai of Shirdi, the king in tattered clothing.

After the aarti all would be fed. Baba would wash His hands, face and feet, and then Baba would mix the food, one part food, one part milk, a little sugar, little roti and would mix the food well, all the time praying, and then that food would be sent out as prasad, which would be devoured hungrily by His devotees. Till RadhaKrishna Ayi was in the body, Baba would send food for her, as Ayi only ate food Baba would send as prasad. Very often more than two hundred devotees would be fed a hearty meal and then sent home.

Baba would sit with ten to twelve of His inner circle and very often Tatya, Ramachandra Patil and Bayaji would sit on His left, while a fakir of Malegaon who Baba loved and would call Bade Baba, Shama, Booty and Kaka Dixit would sit on his right. Tatya, Ramachandra and Bayaji would eat from one single plate, and Baba and Bade Baba would eat from another plate. Baba was very fond of Bade Baba and not only would Baba not eat food without Babe Baba but also every day would gift Bade Baba the maximum amount of money He had got through dakshina. Many would wonder why Baba was so close to Bade Baba and Bade Baba later on developed an ego and would even talk to Baba sometimes without the respect others would accord to Baba but Baba Sai would smile and brush it off. It was a strange relationship which most people could not fathom.

Baba would serve heaps of food to all those present with Him and more so for those who had a family, and those present would take their food and parcel the rest to be sent to their family in Shirdi. Thus, Baba knew what to give whom and how much. He was aware that Shama loved sweetmeats and semolina pudding, and thus Shama's plate would be heaped with semolina pudding. Baba barely ate a few morsels but He made sure all were fed to their heart's content.

Then Baba would wash His hands and sit and be offered a glass of water and a betel leaf with nuts and He would give dakshina of two rupees to Sagun Meru Naik, whose place of honour was to offer the betel leaf.

Baba never took anybody's service free of cost. He always paid far more than the service offered. Remember those days, two rupees was a lot of money.

From one to two thirty, Baba would sit all alone in Dwarka Mai. Nobody was allowed to be with Him then. All would be sent home while Baba sat and prayed, chanted and meditated. He had a bag of coins and often He would at this time remove the coins and rub them gently and softly say, 'This is for Kaka, this is for Shama, this is for . . .' Nobody knew why. If somebody would come inside Baba would like a child quickly put the coins back and hide the bag. Nobody really understood the significance of this tradition but, well, Baba was Baba. He had His reasons and His reasons were good enough for one and all. Also, during this time Baba would stitch His kafni, which so often was torn at various places.

Caiz, seeing Baba old and feeble and make an effort to stitch His kafni, would invariably begin to cry. He found it strange that here was the world willing to serve Him but Baba quietly served Himself. He loved His Old Man.

At two thirty once again He would go to Lendi Gardens,

following the same procedure, and return around four. Once again His devotees would gather. Some were given permission to leave for their homes. Some were denied permission to leave. Blessings were given, parables told. In the evening Baba would stand with His back to the boundary wall of Dwarka Mai and meet His devotees and passers-by. He would inquire about their families. He had now been in Shirdi for nearly sixty years. He was the presiding God and still considered by many as the mad fakir and was loved by one and all though most of them had got their fair share of abuses and thrashings. Shirdi was Baba and Baba was Shirdi.

Knowing He was with them through the worst times, the families living in Shirdi had a sense of such strong security that famine, droughts, plagues, natural and unnatural disasters all were taken in stride, with the imposing but gentle presence of their Baba Sai; He was their Emperor and as long as He was with them, all was well. Baba would often, when the season permitted, as He would not change His routine or timing for anything, watch the sun setting from afar and the glow of the setting sun would caress His face and body, as though seeking permission to set and Baba would be lost in the moment and very often Caiz, seeing this sight, cried and cried.

Baba would, as His time approached for His final samadhi in this body, time and again tell one and all that He was tired, that the vendors troubled Him too much and that He was going to leave Dwarka Mai.

His devotees would then have to coax Him to return and like a child He would have to be cajoled into becoming calm and seated in Dwarka Mai.

What Caiz realized was that when Baba said He wanted to leave Dwarka Mai, He meant Baba wanted to leave His body. That He was tired was obvious. Taking on the suffering of countless devotees and the responsibilities of those devotees had tired His physical frame. By saying that the vendors troubled Him, Baba meant the illusions of attachment and the karmic grief of His devotees troubled Him. Anyway, Caiz would see Baba walk away and His devotees pleading and cajoling Him back into the physical Dwarka Mai, Baba's representative of His physical self. Tatya would tell Baba, I will thrash those vendors. You don't worry. And if You have to go, let us both go tomorrow, now today it is already late, come rest now, and Baba would curse, abuse and then relent.

Then in moments Baba would forget all the commotion He had created and would be smiling and talking to His devotees.

He would once again take a short stroll through the streets of Shirdi and all would be present in lines and He would bless one and all. At six again the bells would be rung and by six thirty the evening aarti would take place. Then again Baba would sit with His devotees and once again singers, dramatists, various artists would perform in front of Baba and Baba would give them each two rupees for their time and love. And then by eight at night He would distribute all the dakshina He had collected, as told before, which would come to sometimes nearly four hundred rupees, which was a king's ransom, to one and all present.

He used to give fifty-five rupees to Bade Baba, thirty-five rupees to Tatya, seven rupees to Jante, four rupees each to Bayaji Patil and Bhogoji Shinde and then to the many

Sufis and sages and beggars and also one rupee each to the newlyweds. Every night, Ramachandra Patil would give Baba four pieces of crystallized sugar and Baba would give him four rupees in turn. The money given to Tatya allowed Tatya to buy land and become a prosperous personality in Shirdi. Baba would tell one and all, eat but don't defecate, meaning use the money well and digest the money well. Eat means consume, and don't shit it out, meaning do not waste the money on various pleasures. Use what is given well. Those who did, prospered and even now do so. Those who did not, soon after Baba's samadhi, became paupers.

Baba barely kept a rupee for Himself, and that too was to buy oil for the lamps and tobacco for His chillum. So the One who was richer than the Governor of India during the day, slept as a humble fakir at night. The British authorities wanted to tax Baba for His income but realized it may not be possible: how does one tax somebody who sleeps with barely a rupee in His pocket each night, though during the day could give any Britisher a run for his money!

Tatya would then around eight or eight thirty get a roti with some milk and Baba would eat a few morsels and then make sure all those who were with Him were fed like kings. Baba would bless one and all and send them home. If He stayed at night in Dwarka Mai, Mahalsapati would remain with Baba.

The alternate nights that Baba spent at Chavadi were slightly different. After dinner Baba would sit, while RadhaKrishna Mai, till she was in the body until two years before Baba took mahasamadhi, and Abdul would sprinkle water on the path Baba would walk from Dwarka Mai to

Chavadi so that dust would not rise and disturb Baba and, as Baba suffered from asthma, the dust would not irritate or create a breathing problem for our Baba.

Then the street would be decorated with rangoli, artistic coloured designs, then Tatya would come and request Baba to visit Chavadi. Baba would ignore Tatya. So Tatya would lift Baba tenderly and then place a gold-coloured shawl around Baba's shoulders. Tatya to Baba's left and Mahalsapati to Baba's right—all three would slowly leave Dwarka Mai but before leaving, Baba would with His right foot put more wood into the Holy Fire and with His right hand extinguish the oil lamp burning inside Dwarka Mai.

Then Tatya holding Baba's left hand and Mahalsapati holding Baba's right hand would start moving towards Chavadi which in reality is not more than thirty- or forty-odd feet from Dwarka Mai.

The moment Baba climbed down the stairs of Dwarka Mai, Pilaji Gurve would begin to play the shehnai and the devotees gathered would start singing bhajans and Shamkarna, Baba's favourite horse, who was beautifully adorned, would lead the procession. Even Shamkarna seemed to bask in the glory of the moment. Then the palanquin containing Baba's padukas or holy footwear would follow Shamkarna.

This palanquin too has a story: RadhaKrishna Mai had wanted Baba to be accorded with all royal honour and thus she had organized the palanquin to be brought in. The first time it had been brought Baba had created a lot of fuss and after abusing one and all had allowed the palanquin to be placed in the courtyard of Dwarka Mai. One night robbers stole the palanquin and when Baba woke up He was as happy as a child not having to go to school and Shama had said to Baba, 'What kind of God are You that You allow Your own palanquin to be stolen under Your very nose!' and Baba had muttered that He did not need all this stuff but eventually He had to relent to the wishes of His devotees and thus allowed this elaborate routine every time He walked to Chavadi.

Thus, while Baba slowly walked to Chavadi, songs, music and the loud cry of 'All hail Sai Baba, the King' would resound in the air, while devotees threw flowers that Baba would step on, making certain He did not have to walk on the wet mud. Baba would once again halt where He would look at Lord Hanuman and then make His way to Chavadi. Then Tatya would first enter Chavadi, which was decorated with coloured lamps, and welcome Baba Sai. A seat would be placed for Baba and a plank for Him to lean on. Then, Baba's feet would be washed by Jog in a silver tray and then Shama would make a chillum for Baba who first would take a few puffs then hand it to Mahalsapati and then the chillum would be shared by those present with Baba in Chavadi. Then Baba would be given a betel leaf and He would say a short prayer and eat the leaf and touch the plate and then others would eat what was left in the plate. Then Baba would tell one and all to go home but He would look at Tatya and tell him, go home but come in the night and see me.

The next day once again, only after Tatya invited Baba back to Dwarka Mai, Baba would return to Dwarka Mai. He would never leave for Dwarka Mai unless invited and then once again with all His devotees standing in line welcoming Him back, He would first halt in front of Lord Hanuman's temple and then Dwarka Mai, and then immediately take care of Dhuni Mai and the light the diya once again.

Back in the cave, Caiz looked at Baba Sai who stood and smiled like an emperor.

'What do you think now, Baba Sai?'

'Baba, to take a leak you needed a procession and then to sleep in another shack you have this whole band and baja . . .'

'I am a fakir of Allah but I am the king of the Universe, you maggot.'

'Ya, right!'

When you reach a state of God-realization, you come to the conclusion that everything is One.

Baba and Caiz returned from their stroll. Today Caiz witnessed, as though in a dream, Perfect Masters sitting one by one with Baba Sai. Rabda could not recognize all but for certain he was aware of many who sat with Baba and spoke for a while; some smoked the chillum, or just embraced Baba for long and then left as mysteriously as They had arrived. Though part of Him was still in Shirdi, with Baba and His beautiful routine, he was aware that very soon he would have to witness something he never wanted to see, which was Baba taking the mahasamadhi. Caiz was aware that the time for Baba to leave His body was soon approaching. But now he saw the procession of Masters come to Baba Sai. He was in awe. He was humbled. He never wanted whatever this experience was to ever end. Not for all the liberation in the world.

Baba had told Rabda to sit in one corner and, when each of the Masters arrived, to prostrate himself and then chant a simple prayer that went something like this:

I bow down first to the Almighty Lord, who goes by innumerable names but there is only One Lord and that Lord is the embodiment of both the Goddess and God Energy.

I bow down to the Goddesses Energy in all forms and God Energy in all forms and names.

I bow down to that very Lord within me from the beginning of time till beyond the beyond eternity.

I bow down to the primordial Guru within me.

I bow down to my Guru whom I know with my limited vision as Sai Baba of Shirdi but with my higher vision I know as my Lord and Master, whom I see in God, Goddess and Guru, irrespective of different names and visions.

I bow down to all Divine, Perfect, Ancient, Ascended Masters and Prophets as well as all Celestial, Terrestrial, Physical Light beings who love and serve the Lord.

I bow down to all those who are the embodiment of the Lord's divinity, grace, presence, Oneness, fragrance and compassion.

I bow down to archangels and angels who love and serve the Lord and who help mankind and other beings to love and serve the Lord.

I pray for the Lord's love and protection for all those who have loved and prayed for my well-being and Oneness with the Lord from the beginning of time till now and who shall do so in the future.

I pray for family and friends of this life, past lives and future lives, those on the physical plane, those on the spirit plane and those in between.

I pray for all those who have been associated with me from the beginning of time, who are and who shall be, for them and their family and friends of this life, past lives, future lives, those on the physical plane, those on the spirit plane and those in between.

I pray for all those who are weak, meek, exploited, abandoned, abused, violated, manipulated and deceived, physically, emotionally, mentally, financially and in any other way.

I pray for the old, the ailing, the children, the damned and the forgotten.

I pray for all those who seek true self-respect, freedom and justice.

I pray for all those who have passed over, all those in between, all those who have been left behind. For all those in the physical plane, spirit plane and those in between.

I pray for all earthbound souls.

I pray for all of creation, past, present, future, those on the spirit plane, those on the physical plane and those in between.

Forgive us, lead us, guide us, heal us, protect us, have mercy on us and always be with us. Give us the calmness and wisdom to go through whatever is in store for us peacefully, wisely, courageously, with complete positive surrender, joy and humour in a manner that I and all those who I have prayed for maketh Thou happy and proud of me and us all. So be it as I pray. Amen.

Rabda looked at Baba.

'Arrey Baba, is this a prayer or a Memorandum of Understanding?'

Baba looked at Rabda and began to mutter under His breath and then sat with his eyes shut and shortly after that the Masters began to arrive.

Rabda was in some sort of a daze. Each Master who arrived was love personified. It was as though this meeting was some sort of a ritual, some sort of a ceremony, but Rabda had been told by Baba to keep silent, though His real words were, 'You rascal, at least shut your mouth till I tell you to speak today.' He had also chosen other endearing words but keeping in mind the sensitivity or the prudishness of the reader, let us stick to just rascal.

Rabda nearly passed out when Lord Hanuman entered the cave. It was as though His Majesty Himself had arrived. If Rabda were to choose the One who brought a twinkle to Baba's eyes and laughter to His words, it was Lord Hanuman. There was a bond so real and so ancient between Lord Hanuman and Baba Sai of Shirdi that it could not be missed. There are innumerable incidents where Baba Sai has abused one and all Gods and Goddesses but never ever Lord Hanuman. It is little wonder that He chose to stay at Dwarka Mai, the dilapidated masjid, which was so close to Lord Hanuman's temple. Whenever He went for a walk He would look at Hanumanji and make mystical signs to Him. It was immaterial whether Baba was a Hindu or a Muslim or from some other religion. It was immaterial if Baba Sai knew the entire lineage of the Sufi heritage and always chanted 'Allah Malik' and made the Hindus read books written by Dyaneshwar and Eknath. One thing that was consistent with Sai Baba of Shirdi was His love for Lord Hanuman.

So when Baba Sai began to look towards Rabda and after a while called him close to the Fire and prepared a chillum which they both shared, Rabda inquired as to Baba's love and fondness for Lord Hanuman.

'You know, Shama, who was the closest to me? He was the one who used to answer my mails and collect my money orders and who used to represent me at functions and ceremonies.'

'Yes, the name Shama is very familiar.'

'Once he asked me about Lord Rama and how it was possible that there could be over a crore monkeys assisting Lord Rama in His battle with Ravana to bring Ma Sita back home. Come hear what I told Shama about it all.'

They were back in Shirdi. It was late at night. Baba Sai, Shama and Rabda were present. Shirdi was a small village then and it was dark outside. Only the calls of insects could be heard. Shama was asking Baba various questions. Caiz realized it was way before 1910, as there were no crowds of devotees and that Baba looked in His mid-sixties or so. The beard was still pepper in colour and Baba looked radiant. He looked like a king, royal and handsome. Rabda for a while was stunned at the casual manner in which Shama spoke to Baba. It was more like one talking to a friend and more surprising was the fact that Baba too spoke like a friend to Shama. There was immense love and friendship that surpassed even the bonds of Guru and disciple and devotee. Both Baba and Shama joked and laughed and Baba often abused Shama who too replied in some equally casual and fun-loving manner.

'So Deva, I have heard and it is also written in the Ramayana that during the war with Ravana, Rama . . .'

'Halkat, do not call Him just Rama. Say Shri Rama . . .'

'Okay, okay, don't get all uptight and mad about what I say as I say it with love. Okay, during the time of Shri Rama, there was a bridge made across the sea, with the help of Hanumanji and around one crore monkeys. One crore is many monkeys to have around. One crore is one hundred thousand multiplied by hundred . . .'

'I know what a crore is, rascal. So what is your point?'

'My point is, is it true that there were one crore monkeys who helped Shri Rama build the bridge? Is it true, Deva?'

Caiz understood that though Shama spoke casually with Baba, he was the only one who called Baba Deva, which means the Lord, or God.

'Yes, it is the truth, Shamya.' Baba called Shamya this with love; Shamya's real name was Mahadhavrao. 'Shri Rama had a crore monkeys to assist Him to build the bridge to cross the sea to defeat Ravana and get Sita Ma back. And let me tell you one thing, Shamya, Ramji existed. He is not a figment of imagination. I say the truth sitting in Dwarka Mai that Shri Rama really existed. Believe me, Shamya, He truly did.'

'I have my doubts, Deva. You often confuse me. How do You know they existed? Where could they all assemble? Where would they get food to eat? To feed a crore monkeys is not humanly possible.'

'Chutiya you are. Of course it is not humanly possible to feed a crore monkeys but Shri Rama was not human. He was Lord Vishnu's avatar. Thus He was the Lord Himself. What is impossible for the Lord to do, you ignorant child of mine?'

'Have You seen the crore monkeys, Baba?'

'Yes, I have seen them with my eyes, Shamya. Believe me, I will not lie to you. They were like ants sitting on trees. All of them sat on innumerable trees like small ants.'

'You know what, Deva, you are lying or just trying to bluff with an ignorant villager like me. I have seen you come to Shirdi when you were a teenager. You did not even have a moustache. So how on earth did You manage to go and see Shri Rama and Hanumanji and those one crore monkeys? You are pulling my leg, are you not, O mischievous, lying God of mine?'

'Shamya, you and I both were there. You have forgotten, I cannot forget. You and I have lived many lifetimes together and that is why we are so close. We have lived as friends but you for some reason got caught in the whirlpool of maya and karma, while I kept at it and have reached this stage. So when I tell you, yes, there were a crore monkeys helping Shri Rama, it is the truth. And when I tell you that you and I were also present there with Shri Rama, that is also the truth. I will never lie sitting in Dwarka Mai, Shamya, trust me. Believe what I say. I swear by you.'

They were back in the cave. Baba Sai looked at Rabda.

'So what You are saying is that You were present when Shri Rama was building the bridge over the ocean to fight Ravana and bring Sita Ma home?'

'Yes. I was in the physical form. So you can imagine how much I truly love Hanuman. When people pray to me, often Lord Hanuman comes to them to help them out. Don't you find that strange?'

And then it struck Rabda. Yes, once he was in a sort of a pickle. Those days it was a serious issue but now Caiz could call it a pickle. That is how things work. Those you thought you could not breathe without become a distant memory, and even their faces slowly get washed away from the sands of time. So Caiz was in a pickle. He at night had prayed to Baba Sai, beseeching Him for help, as there was a lot of money involved and a friend's well-being was at stake and not-so-pleasant-smelling goons threatening to do assorted things to his friend's anatomy. But the friend had done what Caiz had asked for, thus it became Caiz's responsibility as well, as he was in a financial mess.

So that night Rabda/Caiz had prayed to Baba Sai. The next morning he woke up literally scratching his head. He had prayed to Baba Sai and Hanumanji had come in his dreams. He saw Lord Hanuman standing in a temple. Rabda was shown to pick up a coconut, some bananas, some incense sticks, orange colour paste or sindur, which is applied on Lord Hanuman, mixed with jasmine oil.

Caiz woke up saying 'what the . . .' and forgot about the dream. That afternoon he got a frantic call from his friend, asking him to please help out or his family lineage would stop at his presence, minus various amputated limbs, which would entail a castration too.

So Caiz prayed again to Baba Sai and left for a ride on the motorbike to clear his head. He passed various by-lanes and then his bike came to a screeching halt. Try as hard as he might to start the bike, the bike refused. Caiz looked around and then realized what was going on. The bike had halted just opposite a Hanuman temple. Caiz realized this was Baba's way of eventually taking him to Lord Hanuman's temple by the ear.

Caiz did as he had dreamt. He told Lord Hanuman that he wasn't sure what he was doing but as Lord Hanuman had shown Himself to Caiz, here goes: Please, please, please help and please, yes, don't let the friend's you-know-what go under the knife.

Caiz returned to the bike which started that very moment.

Caiz exhaled. The Masters work in strange ways! He reached the office. The secretary told him there were innumerable calls from a wailing man and Caiz exhaled in resignation. He called his friend who excitedly told him that though they would have to pay up eventually, there was no longer an urgency. They were willing to wait till funds could be arranged and till then would settle for interest which was not too steep and Caiz said a big thank you to Sai Baba of Shirdi and Lord Hanuman.

'So you understand why you got Lord Hanuman in your dreams?'

'Yes. Now I am confused. Were You, I mean, are You Lord Hanuman?'

'How does it matter who I am, my bachcha? Am I not your Sai? Is Sai not enough?'

'My Sai, You are the sigh of my soul. I don't need You to be anybody or anything but my Sai.'

'That I promise you and all those who truly love me for myself and not for being an avatar of Shiva, Vishnu, Datta, Vithal . . . I only want to be loved for myself, bachcha. A fakir who wore torn clothes but stitched the spirits of all those who came to Him. A fakir who can only give love and nothing but true love. A fakir who is a slave and servant of God and Allah and wants only to be remembered as His slave and servant. Allah Malik. Raja Ram.'

> Eat moderately, eat slowly, eat well, but never overeat.
> Eat how much you truly require.

'Baba, how come You told one and all to pray and read spiritual scriptures? For the Hindus, you asked them to read various sacred books and You made sure Muslims prayed from the Quran but You often even abused all that they followed and threw out so many times all things Your followers considered religious with not the least reverence?'

Baba halted. The sky above was lit up with what seemed to be millions of stars. On and off, Baba would take Caiz for a walk, at various times, day or night. All the while there would be innumerable beings praying. Prayers, it seemed, were a big thing wherever they were, Caiz had come to the conclusion a long while back.

Baba Sai seemed lost in His thoughts. In reality He was hearing each and every being say their individual prayers. He then lifted His hands in a form of blessing and chanted some prayer from the Holy Quran and then after a while He chanted the holy words 'Raja Ram' and then innumerable times He said 'Allah Malik', 'Raja Ram', 'Sab ka Malik ek' (There is only One God). Often Caiz had heard Baba chant prayers in various dialects of various religions. He for sure was certain he had heard Baba say a Zoroastrian prayer, a prayer from the holy Sikh book Guru Granth Sahib and once he had heard Baba softly chant 'Hail Mary'. It was surreal to hear Baba softly hum to Himself and even then the hum was a chant calling out to God.

'Yes, my maggot, did you ask me something?'

'Yes, my Lord and Master with the sweetest tongue, what I wanted to know was according to You how important is it to pray and read the scriptures and go for pilgrimages? I mean most people are so caught up just trying to keep head above water or live one day at a time without losing their sanity that often there is no time to pray, forget reading the scriptures and going for pilgrimages.'

'Good question. Proud of you. Though you look so distinctly intellectually bankrupt, obviously looks can be deceiving.'

'Most humbled, and if there was not so much snow around I would have dived at your beautifully never-manicured feet, but please answer, before I wake up from this strangely never-ending dream.'

'Okay, so you see the stars above, God has a plan for each and every star or planet that abounds in the entire Universe. Nothing has come by chance. Not a single grain of sand is not where it ought to be. Do you understand this, bachcha? Never for a moment think that everything has come about just randomly. There is a reason for every single thing, including every being, and every being has a soul with prana, which is the life force, and in that life force exists the sigh of God waiting to be realized and embraced.

'I agree that most people are so caught up in making ends

meet, where is the time? But most importantly where is the inclination to spend time in prayer and, yes, often, where is the money to go on a pilgrimage? True. We all have to move towards our priority, son, and a priority that comes about to make oneself and one's loved ones live a life with dignity is a noble priority. Mankind is caught up in the pull and push of their karma, their DNA and their priorities. Priorities determine very often the use of free will, Rabda. Thus, whatever one's priorities are, he or she will conduct his or her life, think, speak, act, according to the dictates of their priorities.

'If a person's priority is to pray, the person will pray standing on one leg, travelling in a crowded train, eyes shut, deep in prayer and if one's priority does not have prayers, then there will be a thousand and one reasons where the person will not have time to pray. I agree pilgrimages are expensive and very often tiring, as most often there are so many hurdles to cross and so many wise guys to avoid, who are trying to make quick money in the name of God, Goddess and Master, that it takes the piss out of the venture. And the crowds of devotees, the pushing and pulling, the standing in long queues, where if you are not connected or rich, you barely get four seconds to stand in front of your God, Goddess or Master. Thus most people prefer to not go on pilgrimages. I understand.

'But remember, each place of worship is sanctified, where just being there works on your karma, your mental, emotional, physical bodies and the corresponding karmas attached to each body. It is all done in a manner that you would . . . anyway, you know squat . . . but the fact is just going on a pilgrimage works wonders for one's karmic cleansing. A pilgrimage starts from the first step you take out of your house and ends when you enter your home. The pilgrimage is not about standing in front of the statue or tomb, but it is about you spending each moment in prayer while on the pilgrimage. But I do understand that a family which can barely make ends meet cannot afford pilgrimages.'

'So then?'

'Sitting at home, heart, mind, soul fixed on God, Goddess, Master, bowing down in the mind, prostrating yourself mentally, emotionally connecting with the One, and spiritually already there in front of your God, Goddess, Master, is a pilgrimage too, as you have transported your astral and causal body out there, said your prayers, and then returned to yourself. You do not need money for such a pilgrimage, you need heart and love.

'Prayers can be done anywhere, beta. Yes, you might not have the time to sit in front of the One at home, as you have various duties to perform, but if S(H)e resides in your heart, then just chanting the Name becomes the most beautiful prayer. Let me make you understand a simple way of entwining and tightly sewing God into your daily routine. Do you know why prayers are supposedly said to be recited five times a day? You should know that this concept began long before Islam. Hindus and Zoroastrians have been saying their prayers five times a day for thousands of years. Hindu temples have various timings for prayers and every Zoroastrian fire temple will offer sandalwood in the main fire five times a day, when the bells will ring. Why five times? A simple reason is that at least five times a day you will remember God. Wherever a Muslim may be, whether he or she prays the five-times namaz at least when the call for prayer is broadcasted, the person would remember Allah or remember he or she is not performing the five-times prayers and thus remember Allah by default at least.

'Now how do you entwine God with your very busy schedule? It is very simple. Let us say you drink water seven times a day, and you drink maybe tea or coffee a few times a day and you eat at least thrice a day. If you do not take tea or coffee, you might smoke, or snack or something or the other. Then you urinate and defecate a few times a day.'

'Defecate? You use every foul word ever known to man and You now are trying to get all civilized in Your speech . . .'

'Halkat . . . let me talk. So water seven times at least, chai or coffee three times, food and snacks at least three to four times, piss and shit a few times, thus at least seventeen to twenty times a day you take a halt to indulge the body. Imagine before every time you put something in your mouth, be it water, food, tea, coffee, cigarette, whatever, imagine every time you were about to put something in your mouth, you remembered your God, Goddess, Master, and thanked the One for the water, food, snack, tea, coffee, cigarette, whatever, and said a short prayer like "Dear God/Goddess/ Master, thank You for this (whatever you may be consuming), please share it with me, please do not let anybody go hungry or thirsty for food, water, clothing, shelter, and any kind of necessity. So be it, as I pray. Amen." Imagine how many times you have thought of the One. After going to the toilet, you wash your hands and while washing your hands you thank the Lord for giving you a place to either bathe or use the loo and the water to clean yourself up; once again, you remember the Lord. When you sleep you thank the One and ask for forgiveness for anything wrong you may have thought, spoken or done and seek protection for yourself and your loved ones for the night and pray that everybody has a warm bed, a roof over their heads and loved ones near them when they sleep. When you wake up, you thank the One for a good night's sleep and for protecting you and your loved ones and seek blessings, protection, and grace for the day ahead. Imagine, if you were to remember the One just during these times, how many times have you entwined yourself with the One? Are you trying to tell me mankind is so fucking busy they can't remember their Creator, Protector, Nurturer even during such times? If they are so busy even then, then they better examine their bloody heads, ungrateful hearts and sodden lives. Do you understand this, you dehydrated rat?'

'Yes, O Lord, with honey dripping from His tongue.'

'A person who wants to remember the One needs no reason and no explanation is necessary. For those who do not want to remember the One, there will never be time and no amount of reasoning or explanation is possible. This is the eternal truth. Now imagine if you remember your God, Goddess, Master before and after everything you do and while doing whatever you do, where is the necessity to pray five times, read the scriptures or go for pilgrimages? Your God, Goddess, Master is by your side each moment of your existence. Once I told the same thing to Abdul and the good man nearly passed out.'

And in a fraction of a second they were back in Shirdi, in Dwarka Mai, seated near the Holy Fire. It was at night and

Abdul sat near Baba, Rabda beside Baba and other ethereal spirits all around. Baba began to speak to Abdul who wrote down all that was written. This time Baba spoke slowly, as though He wanted all to hear and Abdul to pen down what He was saying.

'Remember Abdul, for those who are constantly in remembrance of Allah nothing is required. But it is easier said than done. Constant remembrance means even when you sleep, your heart should chant His Name and your inhalation and exhalation should sigh out the Name and then, given the time we are engrossed in devotion to God, why should we do namaz five times a day, in the morning, noon, etc.? If we are all in love with the Beloved, we will go and reside in the mandir, which means the heart, why should we go visit the Kaaba in Mecca? What is namaz? Why fast? At present I am engaged in heresy if I ask what is qalam. When the Beloved is enthroned in the heart nothing else is needed. If we are ever-engrossed in prayer, meditation on Allah, or performing service, what need is there to go to the masjid, the dargah or listen to the qutba? During the eight watches of the day we are engaged in the remembrance of the Beloved.'

Caiz saw Abdul for a while look down at what was written. It was clear that Baba had made Abdul pray through the night. This was Baba's way of teaching Abdul that His prayers should not just be when Abdul sat down with the Holy Quran but also when Abdul did all the chores of cleaning the masjid, cleaning the streets on which Baba walked, washing His clothes, taking care of the five lamps in Dwarka Mai and the eternal lamp that burnt in Lendi Garden.

Caiz understood that this was Baba's way of showing

Abdul the true path. Not the path of religion but that of spirituality and all of spirituality came from loving God, and when you love somebody truly, each moment of the day is passed in the thought of your loved one or lover and if God was the Beloved, then each moment, no matter what you did, would go about in the thought of your Beloved and once you were already engrossed and contained by your Beloved then where would the need be to sit and pray or go on a pilgrimage, when Your Beloved resided within you? Where on earth would you then go to meet the Beloved?

And then something so beautiful happened that Caiz felt his heart, wherever his blasted heart at the moment resided, physical, astral or the damn causal body, would burst. Baba began to sing and He sang in Arabic or Urdu or Persian, Caiz was not sure, but surprisingly he understood every word, just as everybody who was present did.

'We are in the embrace of the love of the Beloved. We shall go and reside in the mandir (heart) and stay there. We will make collections (attract more beings to love the Lord) and think of the non-believers (pray for the non-believers to love the One). We have no interest in visiting the Kaaba. The face of the Beloved is engraved in my heart. Why should we do prostrations? Why do namaz and why fast?'

They were back in the cave. Baba had a big grin on His face.

'Poor Abdul, for a long time he was confused. Here I made him pray through the night and there I was singing about why pray and all that. What do you think?'

'What do I think . . . uhhhh . . . I think You made the right choice in becoming God and Master, my Baba, and You very wisely did not pursue singing as a career.'

'Bastard you are . . . but mera lal hain tu.'

Saying this Baba began to laugh and Caiz stood there knowing for certain liberation and Godhood were for novices. He always wanted to be the dust at Baba's feet and hear the Old Man laugh like this for eternity and beyond.

*When your thoughts rule you, you are like a slave in
your own house.*

'**D**o you know why Avatar Meher Baba on 10 July
decided to keep silent for the rest of His physical
journey? He did not utter a sound for the next
forty-three years. Do you know why He kept silent? Do you
know why so many lovers of the One keep silent? Do you,
Rabda? I know you do, so tell me?'

'Baba, what will I know? I am a man who has countless
times attempted to kill himself, not in this lifetime but in so
many past lifetimes, and it is because of Your word to me
that You will always be with me and You will always keep
me with You that I keep moving on. I know that not many
are this fortunate. I know that suicide is the worst way one
can torture oneself. So You are asking a man who could
barely keep the clatter of emptiness at bay, why the avatar
decided to keep silent? Sort of makes me wonder if You are
tired and would desire a very badly made of cup of chai.'

Baba smiled, but He was always in prayer. Some prayer or
the other was constantly being mouthed by Him. Sometimes
Caiz heard Baba but most often the words were inaudible.

'The explanation that my Meher gave was that He had
been coming time and again, countless times, sometimes as

a Prophet, sometimes as a Master, sometimes as an avatar and sometimes as a consciousness revolution and whatever was needed to be spoken, all the philosophies that were to be revealed, every possible spiritual truth that was to be handed out, each step of the way clearly paved and laid down . . . but mankind seemed and seems to be like a collective gigantic headless chicken running about, from here to there, often in circles, even though the path has been shown and the destination made clear.

'So my Meher told one and all that as all that He had spoken so bloody often fell on deaf ears, it was best now not to preach but to awaken and thus He took the vow of silence, on and off telling one and all He would break His silence, but He never did. Now tell me, my demented child, do you think that was the real reason or the only motive behind His silence? Why did He have to go through over forty years of keeping silent? Do you know how hard it is to keep silent for such a long time? Do you have any conception of how gut-wrenching it is to keep quiet and then try to get a point across, for over four decades? Some people purport that it conserves energy. Yes, for sure it does, but when done for a short while and when one is virtually in isolation. Not when you are in the world, giving sermons, conversing through the writing board or sign language, trying to get across your words silently. And remember when I first saw Him, what I whispered? I whispered, Parverdegar, and what does Parverdegar mean? It means God. It means the Lord. It means the Absolute Authority. Not an avatar but I whispered Parverdegar and who can bring the very Lord in the physical body and make the One realize His or Her own

Divinity? The Perfect Masters. Thus Baba Jaan, Tajuddin Baba, Narayan Maharaj and Upasani were instrumental in bringing God-consciousness into our Meher but first lifting His human consciousness into God-consciousness and then bringing God-consciousness to operate from the human body of Meher.

'So why did our Meher decide to go silent even though He had the most mesmerizing of all voices? He could captivate all by just speaking and yet He decided to give up speaking and embrace silence for the remaining forty-three years of His physical sojourn. Why did He give so much importance to silence?

'The truth is that God resides in silence, bachcha. God speaks through silence. God is realized through silent contemplation, focus and meditation. Love is a silent emotion. Thus God's main vehicle, love, is silent too. There is no greater love expressed to God than that of silent devotion, silent selflessness, silent surrender, silent acceptance. Silence is the key that unlocks not only the doors of heaven but also the doors of self-realization. The soul encased in the thousand-petalled lotus, the blue shimmering identity which remains covered by the muck of cause and effect and noise, within and outside, can only be slowly reached by removing silently one petal at a time all the petals and this too can be achieved by calm, dedicated silence.

'Meher Baba wanted to teach one and all and all His lovers that the way to His heart was through silent love. His way was of silence. He did not perform miracles like Tajuddin Baba, Swami Samarth or your Baba Sai. He went about silently working through love. Yes, He dictated so many books and revealed to mankind ways of reaching the One, but even that was done with dignified silence.

'So, bachcha of mine, why did my Meher choose silence as His main vehicle to bring about higher consciousness in His followers, devotees, disciples and lovers? The reason is simple. He chose silence as, if He had not, the cacophony enveloping the world would have destroyed the world further. He chose to be silent in order to create harmony in the lives of all people who lived with the loud ranting of disharmony in their lives and minds and hearts and tongues. To make quiet the unrest in the hearts of mankind, He chose to remain silent for over four decades. If He had not become silent, the sound and madness of the world would have deafened and numbed the spirit of countless people. So understand, He chose silence to make you live a happier life.

'You asked me some time back how a common man should be in the world and yet be with God—well, the first step is to be silent within. You can speak little but if there is so much noise going on within you, in reality you are a very loud person though you may speak softly and rarely. Thus real silence starts from within. But even silence can be the calming, spiritual kind and then silence can be the most offensive, aggressive and self-destructive type.

'Calm silence heals you, nourishes you, empowers you and allows you to play out your cards in the most beautiful manner. If you are silent this way within, then God can implement His true plan through you and allow you to live your karmic blueprint in the most graceful and capable manner. If you are silent within in the calm manner, it means you are in complete positive surrender to whatever God has in store for you.

'So silence is most important but more important than silence is calm silence. If you are silent within, but are brooding, you are hurting, you are waiting, then that is not silence, that is a state of enforced suffocation and gagging your true state of being. That kind of silence is louder than a truckload of animals in heat. That kind of silence is the worst sort. It is usually brought about due to having no other option to be silent, or brought about through cowardice, brought about through not being strong and bold enough to take a stand for what you think is right. That is the silence that cripples your very soul and makes you impotent and shrivels your being and causes tremendous and often fatal illnesses. That silence is not silence, it is the deafening sound of hell.

'But we are talking about the calm, nurturing, positive-surrender category of silence. Meher Baba decided to take the vow of silence to bring about calmness, of thought, word, and action, by the power of His silence. But He was filled with love, overflowing with compassion and laughter and joy and mischievousness.

'Silence is the first element. Before came the Word, there was Divine and Supreme Silence. Thus first came Divine, Supreme Silence and after that came the Word. Thus silence comes before the Word. So the One was filled with Silence and then decided to Speak. This is how important silence is. The human body has five elements. When the physical body is dropped, two elements are dropped too. The element of land and the element of water. Then the astral body drops the element of fire. Then the causal body drops the element of air. Then the spirit is filled with Divine Silence, the last element which has mistakenly been termed ether or vacuum. It is not ether. What is the meaning of ether? If you look up the books it will show up as the heavens, atmosphere, upper air, space, kya chutiye log hain! How can the heavens and atmosphere and upper air and space be called the fifth element? In Sanskrit, it is called akash. Akash literally means the sky. Where the fuck did the sky come about as there is no sky in reality?

Space is an unlimited vision of gases and friction of all that which floats about in the cosmos. Why would we be made up of that? Why would the spirit bodies need air or upper air or atmosphere or the sky? No, ether in reality means silence. The first of all elements and the last of all elements before each one merges with the One. Silence is the sigh of God. Remember this, you bloody idiot.'

'Ehhhh. I am silent. You are the noisy one.'

'So where was I . . .'

'You said, "Remember this, my noble, silent child . . ."'

'Keep quiet—so first comes silence within. Calm silence. Which means your mind is silent. Which means you have your mind under your control and not the other way round where your mind has you by your bollocks and you have no say in anything. Whatever noise your mind wants to create, it will create, and you follow like a goat going to the slaughterhouse. So first comes silence of the mind.

'Then comes silence of the heart. Expectations of how people should behave, how a loved one must speak or reciprocate, how you react to any situation or a comment or an individual or a prejudice or a dogma or a custom or religious-society-family thought patterns is decided by how silent your heart is. When you stop reacting to situations emotionally, but react in a positive, silent manner, and not, once again, in a defeatist or angry-silent manner, then an individual has achieved silence of the heart. Immediately you will stop judging people. To judge, my child, is the most unspiritual act one can commit. It is as bad or worse than stealing, cheating, manipulating, lying, as when you judge, you create duality and divide and you push away the vibration of Oneness. Anything that pushes away Oneness and invites discord or duality is a horrifying deed. And when you judge somebody, you are in reality judging God as God is in everybody and more important God has created everybody and by judging or being condescending, you are telling God that He has messed up, He has made something inferior and He has created something that has a default. My son who resembles a fossil, remember this, God is aware of each and every thing and of each and every creation. So when the heart too is beautifully silent, the heart will be in the state of calm positive surrender and centredness.

'So the mind, which is the Receiver, Transmitter and Treasurer, is silently going about its work. The heart which is the storehouse of all emotions is silently observing everything and is like a placid lake at springtime. If both mind and heart are silent, then the tongue eventually will follow suit and start behaving its fucking self. Remember one thing, bachcha, ninety per cent of problems come about with what goes in the mouth and what comes out of it.

'*The tongue has sent more people into the bowels of hell than most of the damned vices. Just as there have been more*

deaths in the name of God than in the name of the devil,
similarly, most of the karmic debt of most people is due to
the tongue. Do you want to know the greatest mantra of all
mantras for one's fastest spiritual growth?'

'Is this a trick question?'

'Nope.'

'Hooookays, tell me the greatest mantra of all mantras.'

'The greatest mantra of all mantras is "Shut up". If you
can keep your mouth shut, you will be doing the greatest
service for your karmic evolvement. When you keep your
mouth shut, you automatically stop reacting to situations and
by not reacting to situations, ninety per cent of your issues
will be either sorted or be easy to sort out. So when the mind
and heart are in the state of positive silence, automatically the
tongue will follow and the individual will be relatively more
silent. But remember, we do not have an issue about talking.
When Sufis or sadhus say, "talk less," what they truly mean
is gossip less, slander less, or how do you put it nowadays,
bitch less. Slander, like judging, is something looked down
upon by God and Master. Slander or gossiping or trying to
put somebody down is once again a vice that comes high
in the order of moral and spiritual bankruptcy. When you
gossip or indulge in slander, you are like a pig eating its own
shit. It is something I truly dislike, it truly saddens me. When
somebody gossips and puts somebody not present down, it
breaks my heart. Remember this always. When you do all
this . . .'

'When have I done all this . . .'

'Arrey maderchaud, I mean when mankind does all this
it breaks my heart. So, the silence of mind, heart and tongue

makes up the pillars for spiritual growth, pleasing your God and Master and also enriching your life. Imagine not being in control of your mind and the innumerable thoughts. Not being in control of the bursts of emotional ups and downs. Not being in control of your tongue. If that is not hell, what is? And then imagine the life of peace, calmness and serenity if you are in control of your mind, heart and tongue . . . and how will you be in control of these three gateways? It is through the embrace of silence. So Meher Baba became silent for forty-three years.

'Of course the people who now take care of His samadhi do not understand all this, so they go about hushing everybody who even whispers near His samadhi or will prevent even a child from laughing aloud. Arrey, for God's sake, understand your Master and His greatness. But what to do? They have cloaked me up from head to arse to toe in gold, a fakir like me, and my Meher's silence they have equated to deathlike moroseness.

'So, my child, silence is paramount. Silence is not just golden. Silence is Divine. But remember, spirituality means spreading the Light and spreading Divine Joy. So silence should not be equated to sullenness or being all stuck up or grumpy. Just as detachment should not be equated with aloof behaviour.'

'Tell me, Baba, You and other Masters and Sufis and sages keep telling one and all, eat less, talk less, sleep less; how does a normal man go about doing all this? You explained to me why one should eat less and how fasting is for those solely in the pursuit of God and not those living in the world with family and animals . . . sorry, family and children . . . but are you trying to tell me that those in the world cannot or should not have the One and spiritual growth as priority?'

'Listen, bachcha of mine. According to me, wherever you are, whichever station life has placed you in, rich, poor, middle class, married or not, family or alone, children or none, businessman or a coolie, pauper or a king, doctor or a soldier, man or woman or eunuch, a priest or a prostitute, the purpose of every being is to realize Oneness with the Creator, to live in perpetual gratitude to the One and to love and share his or her love and compassion with those in need of it. That is and should remain the main priority. If that is your main priority everything else will follow. Do you understand what I am saying, daft child of mine? Good. I love you too. So as I was saying, if your priority is right, which let us call your Soul Priority, then all other priorities which follow will be complementary priorities. What does complementary mean? It means those that support the main priority and enhance or work in tandem with the main priority. So if your main priority is to cure people and save lives, why would you become a soldier or a fighter pilot? Does not make sense. In the same way, if your main priority is to make your God, Goddess and Master happy and proud of you, you will do all in your capacity to lead a life that makes the One happy and proud of you.

'So I agree, this philosophy of eat less, speak less and talk less, it represents the basic requirements for any Sufi or Buddhist or monk or yogi. Basic. But then you will say these spiritual chaps have no worldly work or responsibility so for them how does it matter whether they eat less and fart more or become recluses or do not sleep much, as the next day they have no office to attend to or children to take care of. But you must understand that the path of spirituality, especially under a Master, is countless times more difficult and tiring than the path of a householder or one who lives in the world. I have been hung head down in a well for hours to experience through the grace of my Master a spiritual experience and truth. I have lived for a long, long, long time on leaves, with no food to eat. I have worked for my Guru and toiled through the day and prayed all through the night, barely sleeping for an hour or two and the next day being fresh to go about life, and then again sleeping for two hours, and then again, and again and again, and remember—fasting on leaves or scraps of food. Not just me. You will say I am this and I am that so what is so difficult for me but this has been done and is being done and will be done by countless seekers all over the world for all time to come. You need to empty yourself to be filled with Him. You need to be constantly in prayer, even when working, to be connected with Him, you need to spend much time taking His Name, rather than spending time in gossip and idle chatter. When you do all of these three things, you slowly open the door and take a small step within and begin to hear the Universal Heart Throb. That Cosmic Sigh. That whiff of Divine Fragrance.

'But you will say these are seekers conditioned for all this. What about the common man or householder? Well, it is a simple thing. Lahiri Mahasaya, Sant Ramdas, Sant Tukaram, all were householders. They worked for a living. They occupy seats of the highest of the high in the spiritual hierarchy. My Nanak and the Gurus of Sikhism had families and worked for a living. Prophet Zarathustra, the first

Prophet, worked, taught, had a family. So basically what were They all trying to show one and all? That family is not a deterrent to spiritual growth. In fact, living in the world allows one so much more of a platform and springboard for spiritual growth.

'Who has asked anybody to fast? But then, have I asked anybody to eat himself or herself to either early death or innumerable illnesses? Have I told anybody to sleep so much that you resemble an extended feature of your bed? To talk so much and gossip and slander and bad-mouth and be filled with noise within and outside till even your very own guides and Masters want to shut Their ears? You are a family person, eat sensibly, eat to nourish yourself, not to grow another kidney. Eat to enjoy, not to deprive. Eat to entertain, not to derail your quality of life. So when you limit your food consumption, automatically the body has energy left for pursuits other than digestion. You feel light and not sluggish. You do not feel so sleepy.

'So anybody can eat a little less. Eat sensibly. Eat just enough to nourish yourself. That itself will bring about change in the physical, mental, emotional and spiritual arenas of your life.'

'Karena?'

'What?'

'You said spiritual karena?'

'You legitimate son of an ape, I said spiritual arena . . . shut up, not a word—so even a householder, if seeking spiritual progress, can eat just enough to nourish the body. The body's metabolism is always high when you think of God and chant His Name. The Goddess, God, Master Energy burns a lot of blood and water within. So do not worry about the physical aspects of the body. Also, do not keep yourself hungry. Eat small meals but eat light.

'Then comes "Sleep less". Well, how much sleep is truly required for healing the body and giving adequate rest to the body. Four hours? Six hours? That depends upon you. The more you pamper the body, the more hours it will need. The point is, the more hours you sleep, the more hours you spend without chanting God's Name, without praying to the Goddess, without thinking of your Master. It is as simple as that. Now you decide how many hours you want to spend without your God, Goddess and Master. That is your personal call. You want to spend virtually one-third of a lifetime away, blissfully in sleep. Then God knows how much of a lifetime you spend shitting, pissing, gossiping, eating, drinking, worrying, slandering, envying, lusting, manipulating, deceiving, bullshitting, and on other really important activities . . . so how much time is left for our Lord and Master?

'Eat a little less, sleep a little less, and increase substantially the calm silence within your mind and heart and if possible, talk a little less, by which I mean, dim the clatter in the mind, heart and tongue. Try to avoid slandering, gossiping, fighting and, in short, eating shit.

'So whether you are a monk or a sweeper with a family of seven, you can if you want to walk the path calmly, making the One happy and proud of you and, Rabda, I know you haven't gone to sleep, you rascal.'

Both the men then began to giggle like schoolboys, while passing the chillum back and forth.

True faith and patience is living God by truly loving God, Goddess and Master.

The moment Caiz had been dreading had arrived. Though Baba had said nothing, Caiz knew Baba was showing him the process of Baba leaving His physical body.

The first instance took place two years before Baba's samadhi, which was in the year 1916. People had crossed the village border to enter Shirdi to pay their respects to Baba and the moment they arrived, Baba flew into a rage, which not many had seen before. It was Vijayadasami day or Dussehra, and two years later on the same day, Dussehra, Baba would take samadhi.

Baba not only removed His bandana, which He rarely did in front of devotees, but tore His kafni, removed His langot, and threw them all into Dhuni Mai. He was upset over two things. First and foremost was the fact that most people only came to ask for material and temporal help. Nobody, it seemed, or a mere handful, came to Baba out of pure love and to seek spiritual guidance. He was really tired of the constant flood of people wanting everything but the pure gems that He wanted to distribute.

The second reason for His anger was the incessant debate

about Baba's religion. It was as though it mattered more than Baba's very Oneness with the Almighty. The One who has merged with the Creator is beyond religion. Religion becomes redundant for those who have crossed the ocean of maya (illusion) and karma (one who is no longer affected by the law of cause and effect), but for most it mattered immensely to know Baba's religion. So Baba became naked and abused one and all, saying that if by being naked the question of His religion was answered, then go ahead and look at Him.

Of course, nobody dared to look at Baba. Caiz saw the people gathered actually scared witless and shivering at Baba's wrath. It was Bhagoji who, though he was in extreme discomfort that day, with pus oozing from his body, came and tied the undergarment.

Bhagoji told Baba, 'Baba, today is Dussehra, the day of Simolanghan.' Baba looked at one and all and said, 'This is my Simolanghan,' the crossing of the border. Baba took an hour to calm down and most people were certain that the Chavadi procession would not take place as it was already an hour to midnight. But Baba, having calmed down, wore a new kafni, then behaved as though not a thing had transpired. Thus, two years to the exact day of Dussehra, the tenth day of celebrations of Ten Auspicious Nights of the Goddess, Ma Durga, Baba had already decided His day of passing over.

Thus, by stripping bare, Baba had in His own way announced the beginning of the end of His physical body.

Then in the same year, 1916, Ramachandra Patil became critically ill. There was little hope of him surviving the illness. One night, Ramachandra dreamt that Baba Sai visited him.

Ramachandra fell at Baba's feet in happiness and sorrow of leaving Baba soon due to his illness. Baba Sai caressed him and told him not to worry as Baba had torn away the warrant of his certain death, but two years from now, Baba's close devotee, Bayaja Ma's son, would not survive.

Ramachandra woke up and realized the illness had begun to abate considerably and in a few days he was as fit as a constipated horse, but Baba had told him clearly in the dream to keep this a secret as Tatya would not be able to take the news of his impending death.

Then, in August 1918, the brick given by Baba's Guru broke and Baba was inconsolable, telling one and all that this was not just a brick, but His companion, the physical reminder of His Guru, and with the breaking of the brick, His final connect with the gross five-elemental world itself had broken. Baba had through these years kept the brick safe, always close to Him, often using the brick as a pillow, and no matter where He was, the brick would be with Him. Though the brick was fixed by gold and silver threads and other binding material, Baba was clear that His time had come now.

Baba had given permission to Booty to build a temple near Dwarka Mai in 1915. Thus, it was clear that Baba Himself chose His final resting place. Of course, all assumed a grand temple was being built by Booty in honour of his God, Lord Krishna. Not many realized that by naming the masjid, Dwarka Mai, the abode of Lord Krishna, Baba was going to take care of His children after He dropped His body, from the land meant for Lord Krishna.

Caiz had, since he was a child, wondered about the

connect between Baba and Lord Krishna. Why would a
mosque be given the name Dwarka Mai and why would a
temple for Lord Krishna become the final resting place for
Baba's body? Obviously there was a deep connect between
Baba and Lord Krishna.

Baba would every day while passing on His daily rounds
to beg, look about, and give His suggestions and commands
on the ongoing work. He had told Booty that when the
temple was built, they would live in it, play and for ever
afterwards live in joy.

Four months before Baba took samadhi, He sent a direct
indication of Him passing over. It was in the month of July
that Baba through one of His devotees, Kasim, son of Bade
Baba, and Imam Chota Khan, sent a garland of flowers to
a close friend, Bannemiya. Bannemiya was a known pir or
wali, a friend of Allah, and Baba had spent time with Him,
after Baba had left Shirdi for the first and last time only to
return after four years. These four years, Baba had travelled
to Aurangabad and other places, and had met a number of
His friends from past lives. Bannemiya looked up at the sky
and tears began to roll down His cheeks.

'Nau din, nau tarikh, Allah miya, apne duniya le jayega,
marzi Allah ki.' Or, On the ninth day and ninth night, Allah
will call Me to His world, it is the will of our Allah. As per
the Islamic calendar, the ninth day and ninth month, called
the Night of the Massacre, was in the holy month of Ramzan
and was also Dussehra.

In August, Baba told Hemadpant, the author of Baba
Sai's biography, who was blessed by Baba to write the Book,
to drink the glass of buttermilk offered by Baba to him, as

Hemadpant would not get an opportunity ever again. This was the last glass of buttermilk given by Baba to Hemadpant.

In August, all of a sudden Tatya fell ill. He began to cough blood and slowly his health began to fail due to tuberculosis. Though he was unwell he continued to be his cheerful self and served Baba but by the end of September, Tatya became bedridden and one and all were certain that he would not make it alive.

From 28 September, slowly Baba began to abstain from all food. His close devotees and disciples were worried as Baba's strong frame began to show signs of weakness.

But Baba continues with His round of seeking food from the five homes and also continues to go about life matter-of-factly, but it is obvious that His health is failing, the God and Master of so many. Now when Baba goes about Shirdi, Booty and Nimonkar help Baba walk through His dear, loved lanes of Shirdi.

In fact, it seems as though Baba's body is shrinking and Caiz begins to cry. He does not want to know what is ahead. But Baba smiles and caresses Caiz.

'I am with you now so why worry about what happened to an old, mad fakir nearly a hundred years ago?'

October sets in. The last month of Baba's physical body and fourteen days before Baba took samadhi, He made a Brahmin devotee by the name of Vaze read the *Rama Vijay*, the Victory of Lord Rama, and Baba spent His time listening to the Holy Book. The first reading of the Book took around eight days. Baba made Vaze read the Book again but this time faster. The second reading of *Rama Vijay* took four days. Baba asked him to read it again but after a while Vaze seemed really tired and Baba gave him permission to let the reading be after the third reading. Thus, virtually two days before Baba's samadhi, Baba made the Holy Book be read in front of Him, while He spent His time in meditative contemplation but still very much visible, available and concerned about His devotees and children.

Baba also sent two hundred and fifty rupees with Kasim and Imambhai Chota Khan to Hazrat Shamsuddin, another of Baba's friends, in Aurangabad. Baba had Himself prepared a coarse bread, called poli, and chicken to be fed to the poor in the Name and Glory of Prophet Mohammed and also in Baba's name. This food, given as charity just before death, is also called nyas. The money was sent to be given to those who would sing devotional songs in the memory of Prophet Mohammed, called moulu and also qawaalis, and hearing this Hazrat Shamsuddin began to cry too. He too realized His old friend, Baba Sai of Shirdi, was going to leave His physical shell too.

Thus even before taking samadhi, Baba made sure that both the Hindu and Islamic rituals were conducted, once again showing that He belonged to Oneness. By hearing the Holy Book of Lord Rama and offering food and having devotional songs sung in praise of Prophet Mohammed, Baba was ready to drop His body.

Where Tatya was concerned, his end was virtually near. Shama wanted Baba to go and meet Tatya, but Baba was clear that He had given a promise to Tatya's mother, Bayaja Ma that He would take care of Tatya, thus He would never break His promise and the help He could give Tatya seated at Dwarka Mai was as good as Baba being physically present with Tatya.

Eight days before Baba took samadhi, three dervishes, men of God, entered Shirdi with an ailing tiger. They wanted Baba to bless the tiger. The tiger slowly walked up the stairs of Dwarka Mai and sat with its two feet extended towards Baba who Himself was very ill but Baba's eyes glowed as though there was fire within them. Baba looked at the tiger and both stared at each other in the eye and after a while the tiger exhaled and passed on. The dervishes understood the importance of their beloved tiger leaving its mortal frame in Dwarka Mai in front of Baba Sai of Shirdi.

In the last week, devotees were allowed only to see Baba and seek His blessings from the stairs of Dwarka Mai. Mahalsapati, Shama, Booty, Nana, Gustard Irani, Laxmi Bai and others all took guard to protect Baba from His own devotees, who did not care whether He was ill or gasping for breath. For them the only thing that mattered was blessings and answers to their problems. Baba would protest to allow His people within, but His body was too weak, tired and ill. But when He went out of His usual rounds, droves of devotees gathered in two lines, giving passage to Baba, and like an aged, tired, ill King, Baba would go about His routine.

Two days before His samadhi, Baba stopped going to Lendi Garden and thus two days before samadhi, Baba stopped venturing out in the world in His physical body, even for seeking food. Till two days before He left His body Baba continued with His normal practice of going about His routine, though it was obvious His body was battered and He was physically really ill. People should have understood the meaning and significance of Baba now no longer going on about His routine, but they had such faith that their Baba would remain strong, or perhaps they did not want to acknowledge the obvious, that even Baba's closest disciples did not for a moment think that the time had come for their beloved Baba to leave His body.

Even the last night before Baba took samadhi, He woke up, took His stick, or satka, and banged the ground loudly. His close devotees, who now spent the nights with Baba, woke with the loud sound. Baba was in a rage but soon calmed down. When asked as to what had transpired, Baba told one and all that thieves had entered the house of Khaparde in Amaravathi with the aim to rob and cause bodily harm to anybody who interfered but Baba had driven the bastards away. Thus, till the end, ill health of body or not, Baba made sure His children were taken care of.

The fateful day arrived and Caiz cringed. It was the day of Lord Hanuman, a Tuesday, 15 October 1918. Caiz saw himself as Rabda, seated near Baba. Baba spoke to Rabda and blessed him, saying that He would always be with Rabda, but the young lad, Rabda, who still looked like a teenager, sat visibly shaken. Rabda was aware that Baba would now leave His body in a matter of hours. It was the holy month of Ramzan and also the tenth day of the auspicious ten nights of Goddess Durga, Dussehra, or Vijay Laxmi.

Baba sat with His back to the wall. He smiled at the devotees and though Shama tried his best to stop devotees from entering Dwarka Mai, Baba gave a firm order that nobody was to be stopped that day.

Baba began to bless all those who had come for Him, by

putting His hand on their heads and personally giving them the Holy Ash.

Then Baba turned and looked at Laxman Mama.

'Laxya, chant the names of the Lord softly but I want to hear His Names.'

Laxman Mama began to chant the holy names of Lord Vishnu while Baba continued to bless one and all. Then it was time for the aarti, the devotional songs sung to the God and Master, Baba Sai of Shirdi. This was the last time the aarti would be sung to Baba in His physical form in Dwarka Mai.

Caiz would never forget this moment. The noon aarti began and Baba's eyes glowed. He looked magnificent. Anybody who saw Him then would refuse to believe that Baba's body, His physical temple, was in a matter of a short while, going to be devoid of its Lord and Master. Caiz saw Baba in so many forms. The first form was His beloved Lord Hanuman, Maruti and then Baba became Lord Vithal, and then Lord Rama and then Dattatreya Guru, the three-headed incarnation of the Trinity.

'Caiz, this is who I truly am, the Trinity. I am Lord Dattatreya, because in Lord Dattatreya resides Lord Shiva, Lord Vishnu, Lord Brahma. With Lord Shiva resides Goddess Ma Parvati. With Lord Vishnu resides Ma Laxmi. With Lord Brahma resides Ma Saraswati. Thus, when you worship the Trinity, you worship every aspect of the Absolute Creator, you may call the Absolute Creator Allah, God, Ahura Mazda, whatever Name you give your God, that God contains the Trinity. In the Name of the Father, the Son and the Holy Spirit, the Holy Spirit is the Goddess Energy, the Father stands for God in all His Glory and the Son stands for not only Jesus Christ but all the Prophets and Masters who have realized the Oneness with the Father and the Goddess. God has no form, Caiz, S(H)e is beyond form. Thus when you pray to the Creator, you eventually have to go beyond the limited form of God and merge your prayers and intentions with the Energy, the beyond-the-beyond-the-beyond Energy.'

The Muslims, Caiz realized, saw the Mecca and Medina in the form of Baba and the Zoroastrians saw Prophet Zarathustra and the Holy Fire, while the Christians present saw their beloved Lord Christ. It was Baba's way of saying He was present in All and All were present in Him.

At one, once the aarti was concluded, Baba requested all the devotees to go to their homes and lodgings.

Tatya all of a sudden became completely well. Earlier, whenever Tatya vomited blood, Baba would vomit blood and it would be all over Dwarka Mai. His devotees would keep cleaning the blood off the floor and also dab Baba with a wet cloth. But after aarti Tatya was completely all right. He came running to Dwarka Mai and met Baba and Baba told Shama to drop Tatya back home. Both Baba and Tatya looked at each other. Baba was aware that this was the last time physically both of them would meet. His eyes spoke so much love for Tatya that Tatya began to cry, still unaware that Baba was going to soon drop His mortal shell. This happened at two in the afternoon. Just twenty-seven minutes before Baba took samadhi.

Baba had sent everybody away but His closest disciples were with Him, though not in Dwarka Mai. He was truly not in good shape but Baba kept sitting all the while satisfying all those who saw Him with visions, love, blessings. It was as though all Baba wanted to do was to give His children all He could while in the body.

He then called Laxmi Bai towards Him. He slowly put His hand in His right pocket and removed five coins and from His left pocket of the kafni He removed four coins. He handed the nine coins to Laxmi Bai. He then old her in a soft whisper, as His breath was slowly leaving His body:

'These nine coins keep with you. There are nine qualities required to win one's God, Goddess and Master. The first is absence of false ego. The second is absence of jealousy. The third is to be devoid of attachments which separate one from God. The fourth coin represents selfless service, without any personal gain. The fifth coin stands for having complete faith in one's God, Goddess, Guru. The sixth coin should always remind all the seekers to have a calm and peaceful nature, no matter what goes on in one's life. The seventh represents the constant yearning to know the eternal truth. The eight stands for being devoid of envy and the ninth coin stands for being humble, not to be filled with pride and not to indulge in slander and gossip and finding flaws in others. Only and only then can one move forward towards our One and Only, Creator, our Father, Mother, Everything.'

Baba looked at Caiz.

'Rabda, these nine coins also signify the nine attributes to walk the path. They are in order; the first coin signifies to keep company of saints, good human beings, reading and listening to the words of the Master. The second is reading or hearing the sacred texts. The third coin represents to always serve the Guru selflessly and only with love, without seeking anything from the Guru, as the Guru always knows what is best for each one. The fourth coin signifies that on the path one has to do away with false ego, wrong thoughts, words and deeds and always be selflessly and with love surrendered to one's God, Goddess and Master. The fifth is to spend all your life in prayers and chanting, which is Nam Smaran. The sixth coin means to try your best to keep working on your character flaws and inherent tendencies that take you away from the path. The seventh coin makes it clear that no matter what goes on in one's life, to go through life with calmness and positive acceptance of one's lot after giving one's best to each moment, taking whatever life dishes out to you then as the blessings and prasad of the Lord. The eight stands for having calm patience no matter what and the ninth coin represents faith, the pure faith that your Master knows what is best for you, irrespective of what you think or want or feel. Never forget this, my Rabda.'

Caiz nodded. He did not want to see Baba's final moments, but if this is what Baba wanted him to go through, so be it, Caiz concluded.

Baba began to gasp for breath. He took a supreme effort to speak the final sentence. Something that would become a focal point of love and devotion for millions of His lovers for time eternal.

'I am not feeling well. Take Me to the Wada. I will feel better there.'

Saying this Baba, still seated, shut His eyes and sighed the final exhale. By Wada, Baba always meant Booty Wada, the temple being constructed for the Lord.

Bhagoji was the first one to realize that Baba had taken samadhi. He cried out and all waiting at the entrance of

Dwarka Mai came rushing in. Nimonkar put water into Baba's mouth but the water trickled out. He cried out 'Deva!', and Baba slowly opened His eyes. He sighed out and exhaled and then shut His eyes for the last time.

The King had left His body. He had exactly sixteen rupees in His possession. Just enough not to burden anybody for the expenses of His tomb or the other requirements of feeding the poor after the mandatory prayers.

After the initial haggling between the Hindus and Muslims, it was decided that as long as all communities had access to Baba's holy tomb, Baba's body would be rested in the same place reserved for Lord Krishna's statue. In fact the place already had six feet reserved by Baba for the God of the temple, which for eternity shall always remain Baba Sai himself.

Thus on 16 October at four in the afternoon, Baba's body was placed outside Dwarka Mai. Caiz searched for Rabda but realized that Rabda was no more. What he had failed to see was when Baba took samadhi, countless spirits entered Baba's spirit and merged with the Divine Radiance.

Baba's body was still supple and not stiff as is the case with most bodies devoid of the life force. On a table Baba's body was placed and His body was given a bath. Then a white cloth was spread on Baba's body and for the last time all those grieving lovers of Baba gazed at Baba's body. The fakir who lived His life in a tattered kafni, begging for food, was given a king's procession through His dear lanes of Shirdi.

First in the open ground where Baba's body was to be placed, Baba's lifelong companion, His brick, was placed. For some reason, the devotees broke the already broken brick into pieces and scattered them into the open ground and then Baba's stick, the satka, was placed, then Baba's beloved chillums, a needle and stitching material, with which our Baba used to stitch His torn kafni, along with some spices and an old bag that Baba never allowed anybody to touch was placed. Of course Caiz realized that many by now had opened the old bag which contained a green kafni, and a cap was placed too. Then various layers of cloth were placed and then Mahalsapati, Shama, Dixit and Booty lifted our Baba's body and slowly, with other devotees, put Baba's body into Mother Earth. There was a deep deafening silence as people all around still could not believe their temperamental, grumpy, kind-hearted Father, Mother, Brother, Friend, who only loved and loved and gave and took upon Himself all their problems, would never be seen physically walking the lanes of Shirdi saying, 'Allah Malik, Allah bhala karega.'

'Rabda, remember one thing, I have promised one and all, all my children, that I will through my tomb, take care of them. That I am not this body but I am One with the Eternal One. That if they take one step towards me, a thousand steps I will take towards them. That if they ask me something with true love and devotion, I will answer them. That I have not gone anywhere. That I was, am and will always be the slave of My children. You too never forget this, bachcha.'

They were back in the cave. Baba walked towards Rabda and embraced him. Caiz began to cry. He never wanted to leave his Baba Sai.

Shirdi was Baba and Baba was Shirdi.

Back in the cave Caiz sat and for the first time he meditated on Sai. He followed his breath, inhalation and exhalation, all the while engrossed in Baba Sai and His Name. Now he truly understood the meaning of the sentence 'Ram sey bada Uska naam', which loosely translated means, Higher than Lord Rama is the faith in Lord Rama.

When Lord Rama was guided by the Goddess that the way to reach Lanka was to build a bridge across the ocean to Lanka, Lord Rama was perplexed. How was one to make a bridge across an ocean, in those days, virtually five thousand years before Lord Christ? Lord Hanuman found the task simple. He told Shri Rama that all one needed to do was to inscribe Jai Shri Rama, Hail Lord Rama, on each stone and then the stone would float and that way there would be millions of floating stones and the bridge to Lanka would be built.

Shri Rama nodded and picked up a stone and put it into the water and it immediately sank. So He wrote His Name on the rock and in a second even this rock got submerged. Lord Rama was perplexed. If the rocks He had put into the ocean sank without a trace, how would the other rocks float to form a bridge across the ocean?

Lord Hanuman picked up a heavier stone, inscribed the words hailing Lord Rama and put it into the water and the rock floated comfortably. The scores of monkeys followed suit and their rocks floated too. Shri Rama was perplexed. How did the stones float with just His name when the rocks He had personally put into the water submerged?

It was then that He realized that the faith Lord Hanuman and the army of monkeys had in Him and in His spirituality and in His divinity and Godhood was far stronger and deeper than the faith He had in Himself. Thus, it is all about faith. God is who He is because we have faith in God too. God's power too lies in the faith His very own creation has in Him and Her. Thus, more important than the existence of God is the faith and love His and Her creation have in God.

Caiz sat in a corner and shut his eyes and he knew not for how long he sat thus but he was immersed in Baba and after a while the Baba within him was more intimate and far more real than the One who sat by the very Fire. That is because eventually Caiz had experienced Oneness with Baba Sai. He was certain that now no matter what destiny had in store for him, nobody and nothing could take Baba away from him. Whether he be a sinner or a sage, nothing mattered but the immense comprehension that Baba was within Caiz for all eternity and beyond.

After how long Caiz opened his eyes he knew not, but when he did so, Baba Sai sat looking at him with all the tenderness that creation had ever evoked. It was love that surpassed the accumulated love every mother of every species ever had for her children and in that moment, for the first time, Caiz did not care whether all this was just a dream, a drug-induced stupor, a coma-aggravated illusion or the real deal. He had sipped from the goblet of love and now he was love too and in that love he knew that Baba was his forever, just as Baba belonged to all who loved Him for Himself and not what Baba could bring to the table or the miracles or the karmic manipulations or spiritual growth or liberation or all the bullshit of the balance sheet we try to cover up as spirituality.

Caiz realized that only love truly mattered. Everything else was dhanda and vyapar, business and transactions, in the name of love and spirituality and faith and surrender. You can pray and slit a goat's throat or you can take an axe and slit the throat or you can take a dagger and chop the throat . . . eventually for the goat it was all the same. The Muslims and Hindus do the same and they do it to appease God. Has anybody asked the goat what it thought about a God who got appeased only when its throat got slit?

'I am always with you, Rabda. *Why worry when I am with you? Never be scared. Never doubt. Never worry.* Your Baba is with you always and remember that the Mother is always with you. Step into Masjid Ayi and keep Her blessings in the form of the Holy Ash with you, this is Her blessings and protection and, yes, bachcha of mine, Allah Malik, Raja Rama, Sai Negheban.'

In life force exists the sigh of God waiting to be realized and embraced.

The nurse rushed into the room. Her famous patient for the first time was having a convulsion. Tears were rolling down his cheeks and his body kept being lifted inches above the bed. Two doctors rushed in and jabbed injections into Caiz's body. After a long time Caiz stabilized.

'What do you think happened?' asked the nurse.

'Hard to say. Normally, I would have said it is as though the patient had gone through a horrible nightmare or experience and that the spirit was trying its best to come out of the body. With this guy, who knows, these artists have stuffed their bodies with so much of alcohol and drugs that it's hard to say anything. Keep me informed. I don't want him dead. The publicity this hospital gets from him being in coma is phenomenal. So it is important this fucker is kept alive but ideally in a coma.'

'Doctor, this is not the way to speak. He too is God's child.'

'Oh please. People like him all their lives live in a haze of sex, alcohol and drugs. I have no pity for such people and trust me, neither does God. All his fans have sent snaps of various Gods, Goddesses and Masters, look at this room. It

274

looks more like some temple than a hospital room but trust me, this guy must be in a haze wherever he is and wherever he is no God is going to give him a second glance. Just do as you are told.'

The nurse kept quiet. She looked at Caiz. It was a full-moon night. The moonbeams entered the room and bathed the man with their calm presence. Caiz seemed to be peaceful once more. She had noticed things which she knew were best not to share. She had seen light enter and leave him. She had heard laughter. She had sniffed various fragrances and aromas sitting in the room, waiting for the musician to come back to the world of the living.

She walked towards Caiz, caressed his forehead and for a moment she felt as though he smiled.

'Jai Baba, bachcha, be blessed always, wherever you are, do not worry, my Sai is for sure with you.'

BIBLIOGRAPHY

Warren, Marianne. *Unravelling the Enigma: Shirdi Sai Baba in the Light of Sufism*. New Delhi: Sterling, 1999.

Ruhela, S.P. *Sri Shirdi Sai Baba: The Universal Master*. New Delhi: Sterling, 1996.

Gawankar, Keshav Bhagwant. *Shirdi Che Sai Baba*. Translated by Sangeeta Joshi. Published by Dr Sainath Keshav Gawankar.

Acharya Ekkirala, Bharadwaja. *Sai Baba: The Master*. Ongole, Andhra Pradesh: Sri Guru Paduka Publications, 1993.

Dabholkar, G.R. *Sri Sai Satcharita*. Translated by Indira Kher. New Delhi: Sterling, 1999.

Kamath, M.V. and V.B. Kher. *Sai Baba of Shirdi: A Unique Saint*. Bombay: Jaico Publishing House, 1991.

Khaparde, G.S. *Shirdi Diary of the Mr Hon'ble G.S. Khaparde*. Shirdi: Shri Sai Baba Sansthan, 1918.

Narasimhaswami, B.V. *Life of Sai Baba*. 4 volumes. Madras: All India Sai Samaj, 1955–56.

Anand, Sai Sharan. *Shri Sai: The Superman*. Shirdi: Shri Sai Baba Sansthan, 1962.

Q search .